How does a worker bee direct another bee to the precise location of a patch of flowers, several miles distant? How does a beaver post a no-trespassing sign that effectively keeps other beavers out of its territory?

Animals have always had means of communicating with each other, and man has learned to interpret some of their languages, just as animals have learned to understand some of the signals of man. Today the study of animal communication is one of the most challenging in modern biology. It seeks answers to riddles that have teased men in every age: What are animals saying? What can we say to animals?

In this fascinating book, Bil Gilbert brings together the most recent research and the most important theories about communication between animals and communication between men and animals. He concentrates on the communicative behavior of bees, birds, dogs, apes, and dolphins — a variety of other animals come up along the way — and reports in detail on the investigations of this behavior made by outstanding naturalists.

How Animals Communicate

HOW ANIMALS COMMUNICATE

BIL GILBERT

ILLUSTRATED BY CHET RENESON

Pantheon Books

 Published in New York by Pantheon Books, a division of Random House, Inc., and simultaneously in Toronto, Canada, by Random House of Canada Limited. Manufactured in the United States of America.
Library of Congress catalog card number: 65-20657

In memory of my father, B. LeRoy Gilbert, who will not read this book but helped immeasurably in the writing of it

Contents

How Animals Communicate

1
Two Languages

FOUR PUPPIES were born late in May to our German shepherd, Freya. During the first ten days of their life the pups were blind, unable to walk. The geographical limit of their world was an old sleeping bag which Freya had appropriated as their nursery. When the pups were awake, they were either eating or jostling one another as they attempted to eat. When they were not eating, they were sleeping. Their activities, ambitions, abilities were as simple as that.

Also, during their first days the puppies were relatively quiet. What noises they did make were unintentional, by-products of physical activity. They wheezed as they pushed against Freya, gobbled while they ate, and snored while they slept.

At about ten days, three marked changes occurred in

the puppies. Their eyes opened; they began to walk — unsteadily of course; and they became vocal, making sharp, plaintive cries which sounded as much as anything else like the gabbling of weak-voiced soprano geese. These three new skills, seeing, walking, and crying, were in a sense interrelated since it might have proved dangerous for the pups to have possessed one of these talents but not the others. Before they could see, they had no real need to walk and, being blind, were of course safer if they could not move about readily. The reverse is also true. Before they could walk, the ability to see would have been of little use. All their attention and needs were centered on the sleeping bag and Freya's body, both of which they could know perfectly well by the feel of them.

In the same way, though a little less obviously, the pups' ability to cry out developed precisely when it was first needed. By the time they were two weeks old they were, in addition to eating and sleeping, going off on short exploring trips. Stumbling, falling, they would become hopelessly entangled with chair legs, confused in corners, and just plain lost. Not only when they were in trouble, but constantly while exploring, the puppies cried.

The puppies did not cry out of self-pity, nor as a result of what we would call reason. A young puppy needs to stray only a short distance and time before he becomes hungry, cold, and fearful. The cry is a direct response to these unpleasant sensations. Even so, it may seem at first that the cry is a curious and impractical reaction. After all, crying itself does nothing to feed, warm, or comfort a puppy. It might seem more logical if, rather than crying, a lost puppy smacked his lips or curled up in a ball. These would at least be symbolic attempts to alleviate the conditions that cause the puppy distress.

The truth is, of course, that there is nothing a lost, cold, hungry puppy can do for himself. The one creature who normally can extricate the pup from his trouble and satisfy his physical needs is his mother. Thus crying, passing along information of his predicament, is the one practical response the pup can make.

Freya's response to the distress call of her pups was immediate and automatic. While her pups were wandering, sounding off, she was restless, alert, very much on guard. She would trot between the strays, nuzzling them back toward the sleeping bag, nudging them out of trouble. Strictly speaking, she was not so much coming to the aid of an individual puppy as she was reacting to the peculiar, distinctive puppy distress call. If a wandering puppy is picked up, lulled to sleep, his cry silenced, his mother will lie down with the others quite content as long as she does not hear the cry. In the same way, if the cry of a puppy is recorded and then played back within hearing of the mother, she will continue to seek the source of the cry even though all her own young are safely with her.

The cry of a pup, which the mother hears and responds to as though it could be translated, "need, need," is an immensely practical sound symbol which links the pup to the mother. The behavior is inherited, developed over thousands of generations by the dog family. The pups cry and Freya answers them because each must. The response is indelibly imprinted upon their nervous systems.

Many centuries ago the ancestress of Freya was a jackal-like creature. She, as the wolves, foxes, and others of the wild dog clan still do, gave birth to her young in a cave, den, or thicket. The land was wild and rough. Dogs are notoriously shortsighted and so it would be an easy thing for a foolish pup to stray out of sight, to starve or freeze if the mother could not locate him by his cry. Also there were and still are hunting reptiles, birds, and mammals who could make short work and a quick meal of an undefended puppy. The puppy cry then, when it might bring a snarling mother to snatch her offspring from under the shadow of an eagle's wings, was of far more obvious importance than it was for Freya's puppies growing up on an enclosed porch. Nevertheless the impulse to give and answer the distress call remains in dogs because this reaction has helped the family survive. As Freya's four fat, safe pups cry when they are caught under a chair leg, they probably use the same signal that their forebears did under the shadow of the eagle. The distress cry of a pup is a link across space and time, binding him to his mother. This link is communication, passing information between creatures by

Puppy and eagle

means of symbols. Animals, from two ants rubbing antennae to two philosophers discussing the meaning of the universe, share this ability to forge links of meaning between each other. The ability to communicate has developed, evolved, been refined because there are times and circumstances when every animal finds it imperative to tell others something about its own conditions, needs, or intentions. It is imperative as the distress call of a puppy is imperative — an absolutely necessary tool in the one business that concerns every animal — survival.

Two neighbors, Rich and Jo Zimmerman, live the kind of life that most animal lovers would envy. They own and manage the Gettysburg (Pennsylvania) Game Park. The stock of this unusual farm ranges from penguins to bison. However, to me, the Zimmermans' most interesting and spectacular animals are three cheetahs — a full-grown pair, Top Cat and Petter, and Chief, a young male.

The cheetah is a big, lithe, spotted cat that looks much like a long-legged leopard. These cats are the fastest of all mammals, able to run seventy miles per hour for short distances. Natives of Africa and Asia, cheetahs for centuries have been trained to hunt with and for men. Leashed, and with their eyes hooded, the big cats are led until antelope or deer are sighted. Then the cheetah is freed and simply runs down the quarry. Those who have been fortunate enough to watch such chases say that no other form of hunting is quite so thrilling.

The Zimmermans obtained the three cheetahs principally in the hope of mating Top Cat with one of the males. However, they also wished to exhibit the animals and wanted them to be sufficiently tame to walk politely on a lead in public. Since the work of caring for several hundred exotic animals is hard and constant, the Zimmermans asked me to help with this project of developing good manners in the cheetahs. Long an admirer of these clean-limbed, graceful cats, I needed no second invitation.

Top Cat and Petter, both full-grown, presented no problems. Though both had been captured wild, they had been raised from kittens by humans. Both were exceedingly friendly. Though occasionally their play, sort of catch-as-catch-can wrestling, became a bit rough, their intentions were as peaceable as those of a pair of house cats. Chief, the half-grown male, was a different matter. When he arrived at the Zimmermans' he was about the size of an Airedale dog, and while not vicious in the sense of making unprovoked attacks, he was aloof and obviously frightened.

When I first met Chief he had grown to half his adult size and weighed about seventy pounds. We certainly did not become friends at first sight. As I entered Chief's big cage, he backed slowly and warily away from the door, watching every move I made, his muscles tense. As I approached, he retreated to a corner and there crouched, hissing and snarling. His ears were flattened against his skull, his lips were drawn back exposing his already formidable fangs, his hair stood up on the nape of his neck, and his long tail was stiff as a bottle brush. Perhaps somewhere there is an animal which could have misinterpreted Chief's message, but as far as I was concerned he was expressing himself as clearly as if he had said in English, "Keep away."

It was not that Chief had any desire to attack me (a hunting, stalking cat has a remarkably pleasant, relaxed look about it). Quite the contrary — Chief was terrified that I might attack him. Every instinct of the cheetah warned him that an animal of my size which would advance toward him was up to no good. Had he been free, he would have fled, but caged, he could only retreat until cornered and then make it clear that as a last resort he would fight.

Again, one must avoid attributing human motives and thought processes to animals. Chief did not reason, "If I lay back my ears, snarl, and raise my hair, this man will keep away." Rather, the cheetah was afraid and fear triggered a muscular reaction that resulted in these unmistakable alarm signals. Cornered in a similar situation, a man could argue, scream, threaten, plead, make any number of defiant gestures which might protect him and avoid a showdown. Still it is doubtful if he could express the basic information, "Keep away," any more emphatically than Chief did by his reflexive, involuntary gestures.

These warning symbols are about the same in cat language the world over. A house cat cornered by a dog will respond much as Chief did to me and there is a good chance the dog will keep his distance as I did. Just as the cry of the puppy evolved because it has helped dogs survive, so this behavior benefits cats. Few if any animals are fearless, though we often hear the expression. Meeting another creature which is simply strange or large enough to be formidable, most animals will try to escape. If they cannot, their usual reaction is to do what they can to avoid hostilities. A great many animals have evolved sounds, signs, or gestures which they use to warn off other creatures and avoid violence.

Beyond my reluctance to be mauled by a seventy-pound cheetah, it would have destroyed any chance I might have had for making friends with Chief, if, after being warned, I had tried to come closer at our first meeting. I did the only thing that could be done. I stood for a few minutes, motionless, and then left, hoping I had made a start at the first lesson which any wild animal must learn — that his trainer is not hostile.

During the following days our relations improved. By feeding Chief bits of meat, by avoiding sudden moves, by sitting on the floor rather than standing over him, and finally by playing football with him, I won his trust. The football was invaluable. Chief loved to pounce on the ball, and kittenlike, bat the eccentric sphere around his cage. Occasionally he jumped directly over my head in pursuit of the ball.

In time when I entered, Chief would come to me, rub against my leg, purr, lick my hand with his rough tongue. He began to play, slapping at my boots, hugging me about the legs, jumping up to put his forepaws on my shoulders. In the course of this play he would sometimes take my pants leg in his mouth and give an exploratory nip. Not wishing to encourage this kind of fun, I would give him a brisk slap on the nose and follow the slap with a sharp command, "No." At first Chief responded with his old fear signals, backing off, snarling. Gradually he learned that the slap and "no" were not overtures to an attack but only my sign that I did not want to be nipped. Soon the command alone was enough to halt this kind of mouthing.

Slowly, Chief and I came to trust one another, principally because we were able to establish a rudimentary sort of communication, able to read certain signs and sounds well enough to understand the feelings and wishes of the other. I learned enough cheetah to know how Chief indicated that he was afraid, contented, playful, or bored. He learned enough human to know that I was friendly, that a whistle meant food, "ball" meant a game, and "no" was a command to stop biting. Certainly this was not much of a vocabulary, but it was enough to let us meet in peace, a condition all animals need at times, and a condition which could not be established if animals could not communicate their intentions and desires.

The Gathright Wildlife Area in western Virginia is a wilderness sanctuary in the valley and gorge of the Jackson

River. The Jackson is a clear, fast stream choked with white-water rapids, and one of the best canoeing rivers in the eastern mountains. A canoe trip down the Jackson is particularly interesting for a naturalist, since the Gathright area is a haven for most of the mammals native to the mid-Appalachians.

The Jackson River is an especially fine place for watching beavers. Because the water is swift and runs through many deep pools, the beavers cannot and need not construct dams and lodges, the engineering projects which mark their presence in shallower, slower streams. Along the Jackson the beavers use burrows under the high banks for lodges and the deep river itself serves as their pond. Though the traditional beaver signs are not obvious, the Jackson River beavers are plentiful. It is rare to spend a day there without seeing several of them.

Chief

One day, standing on a swaying suspension bridge that spans the canyon in the Gathright area, a party of us watched a young male beaver "writing" love letters and posting no-trespassing signs along the riverbank. To do this, the big aquatic rodent scoops up a glob of mud with his forepaws and deposits it on the bank above the waterline. Into the mud the beaver mixes grass, leaves, root, wood chips, or almost any debris which is handy. He then shapes the whole gooey mess into a flat pancakelike figure, six inches or so in diameter. As much as anything else this curious creation resembles a child's mud pie and in fact is known to woodsmen and naturalists as a beaver pie.

Once the beaver has worked his pie into a shape and consistency that seems to suit him, he stomps around it a few times, occasionally giving it a pat with his broad tail. While doing this the beaver scents the pie with a few drops

Beaver

of castoreum, a reddish glandular secretion. Castoreum is pungent to say the least, a little of it going a long way. It has been used by perfume manufacturers and by professional trappers making scented lures.

The completed, scented pie, though it is "read" with the nose, is just as effective a means of communicating simple information between beavers as a note would be between humans. The beaver builds his pies throughout his territory and they serve to inform other beavers that the area is occupied. Also the pies tell the beaver's mate, or, if he is not yet mated, any eligible female beaver who may happen along, that he loves or will love her madly.

This behavior, like the cry of the puppy and snarl of the cheetah, is innate (the beaver inherits his pie-building talents), but nevertheless the pie is a perfectly practical way for a beaver to pass along information to others whom he may never actually encounter. The beaver pie is a simple example of one of the most important and useful sorts of communication, messages that inform animals of what has gone on before them and who has been there. It is in a sense a method of preserving historical information. Obviously a beaver pie is not for the ages, perhaps not for more than a few days. Still, as long as it lasts it will inform another beaver as to the mood and activities of its maker. Beavers do not make these strange signs simply to kill time or for the fun of it. This communicative behavior serves to bring about a practical distribution of beavers in any given area. As a courting device it helps to establish a mated pair of beavers in one area and as a warning sign it tends to discourage interlopers who might overcrowd the territory.

The questions, Do animals communicate? Are there animal languages? have fascinated and puzzled men for many centuries. Wizards, magicians, philosophers of old long sought the key that would enable them to converse with animals. Nct infrequently individuals have claimed to have discovered this secret. In every land, in every age, there are stories, myths, folk tales about talking beasts who brought power, wealth, or sometimes disaster to men who could understand them. Not all the stories are told as myths; some are reported as fact, of children who, raised with wolves, bears, monkeys, learned the language of their foster parents. Stories of talking animals persist even in this so-called age of science. For example, naturalists studying the habits of orangutans in the East Indies were told by native hunters that these great apes could talk as sensibly and eloquently as men. When asked why it was that orangutans never displayed this talent, the hunters explained that the captured orangutans remained silent for fear that if they talked they would be forced to pay taxes and serve as soldiers.

Ultimately the answer to the question, Do animals communicate? depends upon what is meant by communication. If communication is defined as the faculty for transmitting information by means of signs in a manner that other creatures can comprehend, then the cry of a puppy, the snarl of a cheetah, the pie made by a beaver are certainly examples of communication. With the possible exception of some very primitive species, all animals make some sounds, signs, physical contacts, odors, vibrations, the principal function of which appears to be to communicate.

On the other hand, we can think of communication in a more restricted sense, as using language as humans do to express abstract meanings by means of complex, abstract signs. Most other animals do not use this kind of language. A few may have limited ability to do so, and with a very few mammals the matter is still in doubt.

One answer, general enough to incorporate both viewpoints, is that while all animals communicate, the means they use and the subjects about which they can communicate vary from species to species. These separate systems of communication might be said to be the languages of the animal kingdom. All the languages are different, but the difference between that used by men and those used by other animals is so great that we are perhaps justified in saying there are really two major communication categories: the language of men (with the reservation that it may be shared to an extent with a few other mammals), and the language of other animals.

The system of communication used by *most* animals, *most* of the time, might be called the language of reaction, while that used by men, *most* of the time, might be designated as the language of reason. These labels are not entirely satisfactory, as we shall see, but they do serve to emphasize the principal characteristics of the two languages.

Many of the communicative signs animals use appear to be made in reaction to some immediate event or situation. Thus Chief, the cheetah, snarls when I approach. My approach creates an inner feeling of fear or anxiety and his snarl is the outward expression of this inner mood. The snarl is not made because he "intends" (as we use the word) to communicate with me. The snarl is a reaction over which he has very little control, to something that has happened and affected his inner mood.

Humans also react to immediate events and express their reactions with what we might call involuntary signals. A scream of fright is a human signal, very similar to the snarl of a cat. However, the distinctive characteristic of our language is not the relatively few reactive signals we use, but the great many which reflect our ability to reason. Our language not only expresses our reaction to the present but also expresses our ideas about what has been, might have been, might be, what is probable and improbable. We can, for example, discuss something frightening long after or before we have been frightened. We can even illustrate what our mood was or might be by giving a scream of fright. For the cheetah this appears to be impossible. He snarls when he is frightened, but cannot modify the signal to inform another creature about the abstract idea of fright or to comment on fright when he is no longer frightened. The cheetah must encounter the actual frightening situation before he can react by giving the fright sign.

We might say that animal languages lack grammar. In most cases animals use and respond only to the "present tense." For example, many animals have a signal which means about the same thing as the human word "come." In animal languages the sign is made in reaction to an immediate situation (the presence of another animal) and expresses an immediate mood (the desire to be followed). However, so far as we know, no animal can modify the "come" signal with abstract signs so as to express the meaning that a man does when he says "has come," or "will come."

Another characteristic of our language is that it is almost entirely learned. Animals also learn some of their signals but a proportionately larger share of an animal's vocabulary is inherited. The snarl of a cheetah is an innate signal. He is born with the ability to make this sign. Chief, for example, was taken from the company of other cheetahs as a very small kitten, yet he snarled in about the same fashion as any other of his kind.

Individual animals can learn to make and respond to signs that are entirely foreign to their species. A dog, for example, learns to obey the command "sit," and learns to "speak" to express his desire to be let in a house. But these learned signals are neither as important nor as numerous in the language of reaction as they are in the language of reason. A great many of the innate signals an animal makes he can no more alter than he can change the color of his coat or the length of his tail.

The language behavior of chicks and children illustrates this difference between these two systems of communication. Recent studies indicate that all chickens have a vocabulary of about twenty-five signals. If a chick is raised by a duck, he will continue to use the chicken vocabulary he has inherited. Also a chick hatched in Germany will make and respond to approximately the same signs as one raised in the United States. The language of chickens is more or less universal. Every chicken can use it, and individual experiences only slightly modify a chicken's communicative methods.

A child, however, born to English-speaking parents will, if adopted into a French family, learn French as easily as he would have his native language. Also, a child, because our language is learned, not inherited, can learn a number of other sign vocabularies — Spanish, German, Chinese, etc.

Until relatively recent times, the division between the language of reaction and the language of reason was considered to be hard and fast. All animal behavior and communication was thought to be indelibly fixed by inheritance, to be "instinctive." Now both the idea and the term "instinctive" are being challenged and are used much more cautiously than they once were. Certainly inheritance is a factor in the behavior of all animals, including men. But in every animal, individual experience (what he learns) modifies these inherited (instinctive) characteristics. Thus a dog has the innate ability to bark, but he learns to bark in different ways to express his reaction to different situations.

There is still much to be learned about how intelligence,

experience, and learning influence the language of animals (as well as how instinct influences our language). Therefore it is impossible to make an absolute division between what we have called the language of reaction and the language of reason. It is quite possible that we may find the language of a cheetah is somewhat closer to our own than we have supposed and that the language of certain other animals may be very much closer to ours than is now thought. It is a matter of degree. Chickens appear to learn very little of their language, dogs a bit more, and men far more.

However, despite the difficulties of precisely defining the differences between the language of reaction and the language of reason, differences do exist. They are real and important. The chances are slim that anyone will ever encounter an animal in nature who will talk to him as Bagheera, the black panther, talked to Mowgli in the fictitious conversations of *The Jungle Books*.

Another of the distinctive characteristics of men is the arrogance of our species. Automatically, one might almost say instinctively, we judge the abilities of other animals in terms of our own accomplishments and needs. An animal, lacking human skills or possessing ones we do not have, is considered "lower," inferior. We seldom speculate on the question, Inferior for what? It is true that a bird cannot draw or read a blueprint. However, it has little need for this skill since it has the innate ability to build a nest with its nose, a feat quite beyond the talent of any architect. For many years this basic arrogance blocked serious consideration of animal communication. Except for herdsmen, hunters, animal breeders, and trainers, who had to learn something practical about animal communication, the whole subject was left to fairy-tale tellers. The "intelligent" opinion was that since animals apparently could not use or understand language as humans did, they obviously had nothing of importance to say. This view has proved to be as much at odds with easily observable facts as the other extreme opinion — that in private, orangutans argue about taxes.

In terms of the individual, the animal languages of reaction may be less flexible than the language of reason, but this does not mean that they are nonexistent or ineffective. Many animals have evolved methods of communication which rival our human system.

Worker bees (of which more will be said later) can, by performing intricate dances, draw aerial maps. These maps can direct another bee to the precise location of a drop of nectar, several miles distant on the far side of a forest. If this seems easy — try to duplicate it. Try to send a friend to the *exact* spot, two miles away, where you found a single violet blooming in a thicket.

Wolves, coyotes, and other members of the dog family have developed a subtle method of communication based on scent messages. In certain territories occupied by dogs there are places where individuals leave a drop or two of urine. The messages left on these community scent boards

Worker bees

convey considerable information to other dogs who may be passing by.

The males of many chickenlike birds will fight murderously, but they (and other animals) have evolved a standard "surrender" sign. If one cock bird has had enough of a bloody fight he will make a sign, take up a position that means, "I quit, you win." No matter how great an advantage his opponent may have, he will instinctively break off the battle upon seeing the sign. This may not seem like a very complicated kind of communication, but we men would be far better off than we are if we were able to develop a never-fail signal which would halt groups or individuals bent on murdering each other.

In short, modern students of animal behavior are not patronizing about how little and how poorly animals communicate. Rather, they are constantly discovering how much and how well animals use their own languages. For centuries the study of animal communication has been dominated by the wizard attitude, the belief that there must be some way to lure, trick, or teach animals to communicate as men do. The current approach is somewhat more practical.

Since our behavior is more flexible than that of animals, it is more reasonable for us to learn animal languages and try to communicate in animal than it is for animals to learn to use human. Working on this assumption, recent observers have compiled "dictionaries," lists of standard communication symbols, for fish, bees, ants, crows, chickens, gulls, ducks, dogs, monkeys, and many other species.

The study of animal communication, now being carried on both in the laboratory and in the field, is one of the most challenging in modern biology. It seeks answers to riddles that have teased men in every age: What are animals saying? What can we say to animals?

2
Say It with a Dance: Bees

Worker bee

THE MORE social an animal is — the more he must compete with others of his kind or depend upon their co-operation for his well-being and survival — the more communicative he is likely to be. Both dogs and cats, for example, are hunters and, as animal intelligence is now measured, they are more or less equal. However, members of the dog family tend to be more communicative than the cats because they are more social animals.

Both the ancestors of domestic dogs and many wild members of the dog family live together in more or less permanent groups. Because they hunt co-operatively, share food and shelter, compete with other members of the pack, dogs have had both the need and opportunity to communicate. Through thousands of years a dog language, based on scent, sound, signs, has evolved which well serves their many social needs.

Cats on the other hand are more solitary creatures. The cat walks by his wild lone in the Wet Wild Woods, waving his wild tail, wrote Rudyard Kipling in the *Just So Stories*, and this is an imaginative but accurate description of a cat's personality. Cats tend to hunt alone or in small groups of a mother and her half-grown young. Not surprisingly, the most sociable of the cats, the lions, are also the most communicative. Lions often live together in groups (prides) made up of adults of both sexes and immature and infant animals. Within the pride, matters of authority and rank must be settled and the lions have developed many signs by which information about status is conveyed between individuals.

Despite their reputation of being the good-natured fat men of the animal world, bears have long been recognized by trainers as being among the most difficult animals to deal with because they are poor communicators. Again the reason is that in the wild, bears do not form large or permanent social groups. Consequently they are not so accustomed as some other mammals are to making signs which express their moods or responding to information passed along to them by signals. A dog, for example, has many facial expressions, positions of his mouth, ears, eyes, tail, which give a hint as to his inner feelings — fear, anger, pleasure. A bear in comparison is a deadpan.

When I was a boy, one of my favorite pets was a young black bear named Sam. We received Sam as a tiny cub, not much bigger than a teddy bear, and for a year he had the free run of the house. Sam was generally an agreeable, well-behaved animal, but an unpredictable one. He had a trick of sitting up and begging in front of the cupboard where his own private jar of honey was kept. In time someone would come along, get down the honey jar and feed Sam, a spoonful at a time. One day I sat down on the floor to give Sam his treat. Perhaps I was slow unscrewing the top of the honey bottle, perhaps Sam was just in a bad mood, but in any event, without any warning or change in expression, he reached out and gave me a healthy smack on the face, turned his back and lumbered across the room, taking up what was clearly a defensive position and attitude behind the table. A slap from even a six-month-old bear is not exactly a love tap and as Sam got older and his paws got heavier, our failure to understand what was going on in his mind caused us to present him to a zoo, where he could live without being faced with complicated communication problems.

Even among humans this relationship between social organization and communication can be observed. The language of a primitive tribe in the mountains of New Guinea is far simpler than that used by men living in more complex societies. The tribal vocabulary is smaller and not so well suited for expressing fine shades of meaning. In a small isolated group, there is less need and opportunity to use the kind of intricate language which binds together our complicated, technical society made up of many million individuals.

THE SOCIETY OF THE BEES

Given this rule that the more social animals usually have the most expressive languages, it is not surprising that the honeybee has evolved one of the most useful and accurate languages in the animal world. To say simply that honeybees are social and co-operative is to understate the facts.

Coyotes, gulls, fish, men are also social and co-operate with each other. Yet, all of these creatures probably devote more time to satisfying their own needs, acting independently, than they do to the affairs of the pack, flock, school, or community to which they belong. With the bee it is quite different. Nearly all of her active life is given over to serving her hive, and in the service of the hive the bee works continually in co-operation and communication with others. Life in a beehive is so closely and constantly organized that some naturalists have claimed that the bee should not be regarded or studied as an individual; that the hive is the basic unit of bee life and that the individual functions only as do the individual cells within a living body. This is a dramatic but extreme theory. The single bee, unlike the single body cell, can function alone, though not for very long and not properly. Nevertheless it is true that in the world of the bee, the hive is all-important while the activity of any single bee is relatively unimportant.

A beehive, in the spring and summer, located in an area where there is plenty of bee food, will have a population of 50,000 or 60,000 adult bees, the fully winged creatures which everyone has seen buzzing about a cluster of flowers. By far the greatest number of these are worker bees, females who are unable to lay eggs. In addition to these workers, there are two other types of bees, queens and drones. Each spring about a half a dozen new queens are hatched and one becomes queen of the hive, the only bee among the thousands who can lay eggs. The old queen may lead some workers away from the old hive to establish a new one; this is called swarming and will be described later in this chapter. The drones are males, whose only function is to mate with a queen prior to the swarming period.

While the thousands of workers in a hive are similar in appearance, they have different jobs. In addition to the

Queen bee

bees who collect pollen and nectar from flowers and those who feed the larvae, there are bees who build combs, keep the hive clean, control the temperature, and guard the colony. Though the work of each bee is specialized, like that of a man working on the assembly line of a great factory, individual bees change jobs as they grow older. During the first days after they emerge from the cells, the glands of young bees produce the "milk" which is fed to the larvae, and thus these bees are called "nurses." When the bee is about ten days old, these glands disappear and wax glands develop. For the next several weeks the bee serves the hive as a construction worker, building new combs, and also as a housekeeper, keeping the hive clean. When the wax glands fail, the bee turns her attention outside the hive and from then until the end of her life is occupied with collecting pollen or nectar.

Since man has probably been honey eater almost as long as he has been man, he has spent a lot of time looking at and for bees. It has been known for a long time by bee hunters and beekeepers (as well as by anyone who has had bees gather around a glass of sweet iced tea or soft drink) that bees can be baited. If a few bees are given a rich source of food they will return to the spot, bringing other bees with them. This suggests several important things about the behavior and abilities of the honeybee. Since bees can return to a few drops of sugar water from a hive perhaps several miles away, they must have a very good sense of what we call direction. Also they must be able to remember directions, at least for the length of time it takes them to fly from the bait to hive and back. Finally there is the fact that the first bees bring other bees with them, but not directly. The new bees do not play follow-the-leader with the first ones. They do not simply tag along behind, within sight or sound. Still, they seem to come directly to the bait, not just stumble upon it. The only possible explanation is that somehow the first bees returning from the bait have "told" other bees how to get there.

It is easy to say now that all of this is obvious, but the fact is that, though men have been interested in and handling bees for many centuries, it was not until 1943 that we found out how the bees communicate. The language of the bees has been described and translated largely through the work of one man, Karl von Frisch, a German zoologist. Von Frisch's proof that bees do have a marvelously exact language is one of the great biological discoveries of recent times. Not only did he add greatly to our understanding of the bees, but his work has been important in the whole study of animal communication. Von Frisch's studies of the communication of bees, as well as of their senses, are a model of the kind of accurate observation a scientific naturalist can and must make.

In making many of their tests, Von Frisch and his assistants watched marked bees not only as they were feeding at dishes baited with sugar syrup but as they returned to the hive (glass-walled hives were used in order to observe activities within the colony). During the long hours of patient study it was noted that a bee returning from a bait dish often performed what seemed to be a wild dance. Other workers who were food collectors would become very excited by these displays and apparently try to join the first bee in her ballet. Many times these spectator bees would then be observed leaving the hive and in a short time they would appear at the baited dishes. These dances had been observed before and puzzled other bee watchers, but Von Frisch was the first to demonstrate that the strange dances were the words and sentences of bee language.

After extensive observation and testing, Von Frisch discovered that there are actually two distinct dances. Depending on the circumstances, a bee would use one or the other of the dances to tell other bees that she had found a rich source of food and how they might get there.

The first of these movements, Von Frisch called the round dance. (See the illustration on page 32.) After a bee returns to the hive with a heavy load of nectar she first distributes her cargo to inside bees, who take the food into their own stomachs. Then the bee who has made the food discovery may begin to dance on the comb. She spins in a small circle making several turns, reverses the movement, then repeats the whole figure. Other collecting bees who are nearest to the dancer try to follow her, jostling each other as they attempt to touch the performer with their own antennae. After the ballerina bee has made several circles, she may move on to another part of the comb and repeat her dance for a new audience. After a minute or two, she leaves the hive and returns to the syrup treasure she has found. In the meantime some of the other bees who followed the first dance will also leave the hive and find their way to the same bait. When they return, they will dance as the first bee did, and other workers will follow their gyrations.

Obviously, because of the persistence with which they were performed and the results of each performance, these dances were not being done simply for exercise or entertainment — they said something to other bees. After a time Von Frisch and his assistants were able to understand the meaning of these round dances. A translation from bee to English might read, "Less than a hundred yards from the hive is a pool of first-class nectar. It smells like this."

Just the fact that the bee was dancing told the value (in bee terms) of the discovery. Bees will not perform their dances if the food supply is ordinary. Only when they have found exceptionally rich food do they tell the others about it. The information about odor was passed on as the other bees followed the dancer. The bees' scent-reading organs

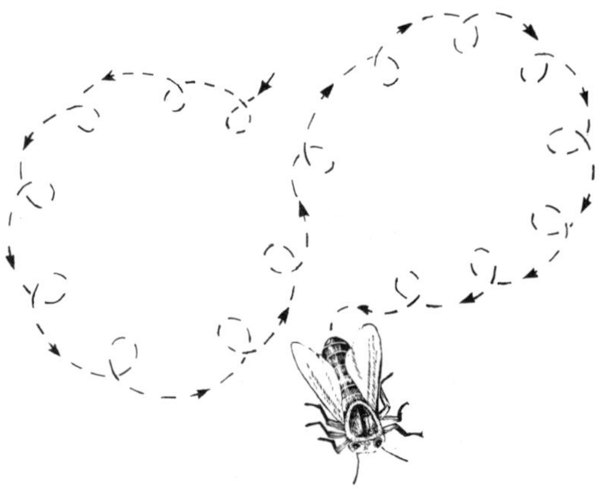

The round dance

are located in the antennae. As other bees touched the dancing bee they learned more of her discovery because the scent of the feeding place clung to her body.

The fact that the source of food was a hundred yards or less from the hive was communicated by the fact that the bee chose to perform the round dance. The round dance is only used when the food is located relatively close to the hive. The round dance does not describe the direction of the food, only that it lies within a circle with a hundred-yard diameter. Considering how many bees there are collecting food and how fast they can fly, it does not take the workers long to scan such a small area and find the prize. However, locating a dish of syrup (or under ordinary circumstances a clump of nectar-rich blossoms) a mile or two from the hive is a far different thing. Searching throughout a circle of this size would be such a time-consuming chore as to make the round dance next to useless. Directions to a distant place are given by the bees through the use of a second set of signs which Von Frisch called the wagging dance.

The wagging dance (see the illustration on page 34) is a much more complicated and meaningful performance than the round dance. Like the round dance it announces that rich food with a particular scent has been discovered, but this dance also informs the bee audience how far the food is from the hive and in what direction it lies.

In the wagging dance the bee moves first in a semicircle, then runs in a straight line between the horns of the half circle, cuts another semicircle in the opposite direction, and completes the figure with another straight run. As she dances on her straight-line course she wags her body from side to side and this distinctive movement accounts for the name Von Frisch gave this performance.

How rapidly the bee performs the wagging dance an-

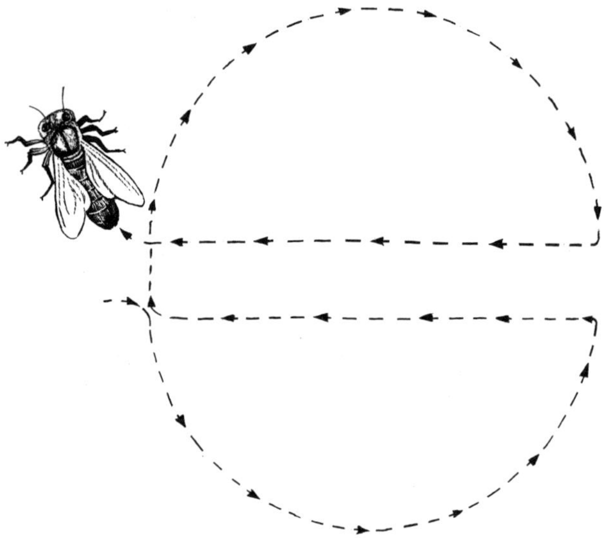

nounces how far her discovery is from the hive. The announcement is made very clearly and accurately. A bee who does one complete wagging dance pattern in a little more than a second and a half tells her audience that the food is about 325 feet away. If it takes two seconds to do the dance then the food is 650 feet distant. If the food is a mile away the bee will take almost five seconds to complete one dance turn. In general, the slower a bee dances the further away from the hive is the food. This relationship between time and distance seems to hold true for any distance over a hundred yards, the point at which the round dance is replaced by the wagging dance.

Not only are the bees who follow the wagging dancer accurately informed as to how far they must fly to find the food, but they are also told in what direction to search. This is done in one of two ways, depending upon whether the dance is performed outside the hive on a horizontal surface where the bees can see the sun or inside on the vertical comb, in the dark of the hive.

If the dance is done outside on the flat landing board of the hive, the straight run of the dance is pointed in precisely the direction of the food. The other bees in flight can stay on this route because they have the ability to fix their own position and navigate according to the sun's angle. Thus, if the dancing bee runs on a straight line which is 10 degrees to the left of the position of the sun, she has told the bees in her audience to fly a route 10 degrees to the left of the sun.

Most of the dances, however, are done inside the hive on the vertical combs. Lacking both a flat horizontal platform and light, the dancing bee obviously cannot point out the direction of the food in relation to the sun as she can outside the hive. How these difficulties have been overcome must rank as one of the most astounding features of the bee language.

In what we would think of as the neck of a honeybee there is a row of fine hairlike organs which enable the insects to gauge the gravitational force of the earth. Because of these tiny instruments, bees, even in the dark hive, have an acute sense of position, what is straight up and down and variations from this straight line. On the vertical comb the bee makes use of this remarkable sense in the wagging dance. If she faces up on the straight-line part of her dance she indicates that the food is toward the sun from the hive. If she faces down, the food is away from the sun in relation to the hive. If she points her waggle run 10 degrees to the left of an imaginary vertical line which represents straight up and down, the other bees "read" this movement as meaning that they should fly on a route 10 degrees to the left of the sun. In this way, position of a bee in relation to gravitational force is translated into position in relation to the sun, an incredible mathematical feat for any animal.

The information which is passed between the bees by the wagging dance is so precise that a man who has learned this language can, after watching a dance, go to the spot the performing bee has described. However, a man can only do this if he has a small pack full of instruments—stop watch, compass, surveyor's transit, metal tape, and topographic map. Unaided, our natural senses of time, distance, and direction are not keen enough either to understand or follow the precise kind of directions by which bees routinely communicate.

After the discovery of the use and meaning of the round and wagging dances, Von Frisch and other scientists made additional observations and tests. These have brought to light still other facts about the system of communication which has evolved among the honeybees.

The basic dance pattern of the bee tells other bees how to travel in a "beeline," without interference, to the food source. However, it is sometimes impossible for a worker to fly directly to the place described in the dance. For example, the first scout may have found food on the opposite side (from the hive) of a steep cliff or tall building. To reach her hive she may have had to make a right-angle turn to get around this obstacle. When she returns to the hive she describes, through the wagging dance, not the route she actually flew but an *imaginary course,* a straight line between hive and food, which she would have flown had the barrier not been there. The bees who use this information start out in a beeline, meet the obstruction that barred the first bee, fly around it and get back on the straight-line course. This ability to change courses and estimate the degree and distance of the change alone entitles the worker bee to the highest marks as an expert celestial navigator.

Wind also affects a bee's flight. A headwind will slow her down and a tailwind will increase her speed. In the dances a bee gives information only about the outbound trip — from the hive to the food. If she has bucked a strong wind she indicates in her dance that the food lies further from the hive than the actual measured distance. In reverse, if she has been aided by a wind behind her she will describe a shorter distance than is actually the case. Experiments indicate that the bee does not calculate the distance on the flying time involved but rather on the amount of energy she uses in reaching a given spot.

There are dialects in the dancing language of the bees, just as there are in human languages. What we call honeybees are all members of one species, given the scientific name *Apis mellifera*. However, this species is subdivided into many different races. Each race uses the round and wagging dances for communication, but uses them in slightly different ways. For example, the Italian honeybee has a slower dancing speed than that of the Austrian bee. The Italian bee switches from the round dance to the wagging dance when the food is about 125 feet from the hive, but the Austrian bee does not commence her wagging dance unless food is 300 feet away from the hive. An Austrian bee will react to a dance by an Italian bee but she will react incorrectly because she does not completely understand the Italian's "accent."

Accurate as the dancing language is, bees cannot use it to describe places which are far above the hive. Von Frisch placed a bait dish in a radio tower, high above the colony, and allowed bees to feed there. When they returned they were completely confused and did only the round dance. The lack of a sign for "up" in bee language is understandable. Curious men can put sugar syrup on a tower, but flowers, a bee's regular source of food, do not bloom in the sky.

The question Why? should be considered in connection with the bee dances, just as it should be in regard to any other sort of animal communication or behavior. The answer is that it is vital for the survival of the hive that bees be able to pass the kind of information they do between each other. The bee's stomach, in which she carries nectar, is not much larger than a head of a pin, but to fill this tiny container the bee may make 1,500 flower stops. Even so, an active hive of bees may manufacture and store two pounds of honey on a good day. The higher the sugar content of the nectar the more honey it will make and the easier it will be for the inside bees to turn it into honey. However, flowers that offer rich stores of nectar bloom, wither, and disappear in a relatively short time. Bees compete with those from other hives and with many other creatures for this nectar. Therefore when a good nectar supply is found, the hive benefits if a number of workers can be quickly mobilized at this spot to gather in the food before it dries up or is taken by some other animal. This mobilization and co-operation can take place only if one bee can alert her hive mates when she finds something that is worth their attention and will benefit the entire hive.

THE WATER DANCE

The round and wagging dances are used by the honeybees to describe the location of food, but there are other situations when information must be exchanged between members of the hive. Controlling the temperature of the hive is another example of a job that requires the bees to work together and communicate.

The bee eggs, larvae, and cocoons inside the cells of the comb require a temperature of 95° F. and cannot survive if the hive grows hotter or colder than this for any long period of time. Adult bees, along with their many other marvelous senses, are able to gauge temperature very accurately and take immediate action when a heat crisis arises. When the temperature begins to fall below the ideal level, thousands of bees spread out over the brood comb, their bodies and the air space between them serving as a warming, insulating blanket. When the temperature begins to rise, the inside, housekeeping bees will spread out so the air can circulate more freely and begin to beat their wings, acting like thousands of tiny fans. If the temperature continues to rise, the inside bees begin to spread water inside the cells and on the surface of the comb. The water fanned by their wings evaporates quickly, producing a cooling action in the same way that a drop of gasoline spilled on the back of one's hand makes the skin feel cold as it evaporates.

Effective as the water cooling system is, the inside workers cannot continue it for very long without the co-operation of the outside workers. Except for what little water may be mixed with the honey in their own stomachs, the inside bees have no supply of water. It must come from outside and it must be carried in by the bees who are experienced outside navigators and foragers. The problem is further complicated by the fact that the food-collecting bees spend far more time outside the hive than within and will not ordinarily be aware of when and how much water is needed. This information must be communicated by the housekeeping bees.

All nectar contains water, but ordinarily the less water and more sugar it has the more prized it is by the collecting bees. Watery nectar is more difficult for the inside bees to convert into honey and normally they are unenthusiastic about accepting a cargo of watery nectar from a collecting bee. However, when the temperature rises in the hive and the inside bees have used up all the water in their own stomachs this normal pattern is reversed. Bees at the center of the hive begin to beg for water from those nearer the entrance and these in turn greet eagerly the collecting bees who return with the weakest (most watery) nectar. The receiving bees begin to dance around the water bearers. Though this dance is not so regular and does not communicate such precise information as the round and wagging dances, it apparently convinces the collecting bees that things have suddenly changed and water, not honey, is now at a premium. The water dance might be translated: "What you have is what I want. More water, more water." The faster the inside bees dance the more excited the collectors become. Shortly they can be observed outside the hive taking weak nectar in preference to strong and sometimes collecting pure water only.

The inside bees must not only be able to start the collectors gathering water, but they must also be able to stop them. Water, unlike honey, cannot be stored in the hive. As the temperature begins to fall back toward the desired 95-degree mark, the dances of the inside bees meeting the water carriers become slower, less enthusiastic. Finally, when the proper temperature is restored, the inside bees stop this dance and cold-shoulder the bees who return to the hive with weak nectar or water. Very shortly the collectors are convinced that things have returned to normal and that sugar-rich honey is again what the hive needs and they should find.

THE GREAT DEBATE, OR THE DANCE OF THE SWARM

When bees go house-hunting they, like the members of a human family, may disagree as to what sort of a home they need. At these times, the nearest thing to an argument takes place in the smoothly organized life of the bees and the argument is carried on in the marvelous dancing language. The dances are no longer performed solely to pass on information but are used by one bee or a group of bees to convince others as to the best course of action.

In the late spring or early summer, when the hive is crowded with both adults and the broods of young bees, the urge to find a new home comes upon some of the members of the colony. As a group, many thousands of bees will leave the hive (after having first filled their stomachs with emergency honey rations), taking the old queen with them. This action is called swarming. The result of swarming is that new colonies are established, the range of the bees is expanded, and overcrowding in the original hive is relieved.

The old queen who leaves the hive is escorted by a swarm of bees that may number twenty thousand or more. Wherever the queen first lands, on a tree limb, a telephone pole, on a roof, or even occasionally inside a house, the swarm settles around her. The great mass of bees crowd closely together, holding to each other's bodies, hanging like a great wriggling beard.

If the bees come from a domestic hive, either they will not be allowed to swarm or their swarming period will be a short one, as the beekeeper will scoop up the hanging cluster and put it into a manufactured hive box. Wild bees, however, must find their own home and the whole important matter is turned over to a relatively few scouts who investigate possible sites and debate the merits of each.

Martin Lindauer, who was a student of Karl von Frisch and is a noted authority on bees in his own right, has closely observed the swarming and house-hunting behavior of honeybees. He found that even before the swarm leaves the old hive, certain food-collecting bees seem to enter a training period for serving as hive-hunting scouts. As swarming time approaches, these bees show less and less interest in their normal food-gathering work. Rather, they can be observed exploring all sorts of holes, cavities, and cracks, the kind of places that a swarm might choose as a new home. These scout bees do not appear to be physically different from the other workers, and once the swarming period is over, they are able to resume their regular work of food gathering. Why and how certain bees become scouts is something of a mystery, but it is clear that, as scouts, they serve the new colony in a time of great need.

When the swarm has come to rest, these scouts fan out to explore the area. When a scout has found a possible hive site she returns to the swarm and performs a wagging dance similar to that used by the food collectors.

The dance describes the distance and direction of the place but the scout also makes known her opinion of the quality of the site she has discovered. The more persistently and enthusiastically the scout dances, the higher the regard she shows for the spot. If the dance is listless and not repeated vigorously, the bee is not convinced that the hole she has found is really what the hive needs. The scout bees have very definite "ideas" about what constitutes a good homesite. By offering many possible sites to swarms, Martin Lindauer found some of the factors which influence the bees' choice.

The bees need a protected cavity in which to build their combs, raise their brood, and store their food. Bees will choose a hive site which is sheltered from the wind in preference to one that is exposed. They will choose a shady place over a sunny one. They will reject a cavity which is being used by other animals, mice or ants for example. In one case the scout bees danced enthusiastically all day, describing what seemed to be an ideal hole. However, during the night there was a thunderstorm and the hollow was flooded. The next day the scouts showed little interest in the house with the leaky roof.

The size of the cavity is also important. It must be large enough to house the swarm and permit its growth but it cannot be so large that the inside workers will have difficulty controlling the temperature. Distance from the old hive is also important. After leaving their old hive, the swarming bees do not necessarily choose the first good place they find. Rather, they seem inclined to go a considerable distance from their old home, even though this may mean passing up suitable homesites. This behavior serves to spread out the bee population and avoid unnecessary food competition between colonies.

All of these factors affect the way in which the scout bees perform their wagging dances. The purpose of these dances is to inform the other scouts and also to convince

A swarm

them. An excited dancer will attract other scouts who follow her dance and then go off to investigate the place she is describing for themselves. If they are impressed they return to the swarm and begin to argue, through their dances, for the same hole.

In time there may be a dozen different dances being performed, each representing a "speech" aimed at convincing the other bees of the merits of a particular homesite. Gradually the most excited scouts, those with the best case, will draw away supporters from the other dances. At last nearly all the scouts will be dancing in favor of one site. Only when this more or less unanimous agreement has been reached will the whole swarm move. In this election, only the scout bees seem to have a vote. The queen and the rest of the workers wait passively while the scouts debate the choice. When a decision has been reached the rest of the swarm obediently follows the scouts to the new home.

The argument between the scouts is not settled hurriedly and may last for days or even weeks. Lindauer describes one such campaign in which scouts came back to the swarm reporting twenty-one possible homesites. During the first three days "propaganda" dances were performed for all these spots. One location, to the north of the swarm, at first seemed to have more supporters. However, on the fourth day there was a shift in opinion and a number of scouts began dancing in favor of a hole in an old stone wall, southeast of the swarm. So vigorously did the stone-wall bees dance their case that by the fifth day they had convinced the other scouts and the swarm moved off to take up residence in the wall.

Unanimous consent is necessary, for there is no way a minority party can split away from the swarm and set up its own house. There is only one queen in a swarm and without her there is no reason or way for the bees to establish a hive. The entire swarm must go to one site and the queen must go with them. Occasionally, however, the argument becomes so hot among the dancing scouts that no decision is possible. In one swarm that Lindauer observed, the merits of various homesites were debated for fourteen straight days without any agreement being reached. At the end of two weeks the scouts simply gave up. The hungry swarm began to build combs in the open, on the bush on which they had come to rest. There the queen began to lay eggs and the workers to store food. If Lindauer had not been there to watch over them, this failure of the scouts to reach a decision would have meant the end of the colony. Even if the combs were not robbed or destroyed by predators, the bees could not have survived freezing winter temperatures in the open.

Even though such absolute failures are rare, the whole elaborate, time-consuming debate of the house-hunting scouts may seem to be wasteful and inefficient behavior, considering that the immediate need of the swarm is to get into a home and start to work. Actually this "elective" method of selecting a hive site serves several useful purposes. The long debate guarantees that a decision in this all-important matter will not be made in haste. The various places being "advertised" by the dancers are visited frequently by many scouts and they thus are able to observe the holes at different times of day and in different sorts of weather. A site which might be satisfactory in the morning may be too sunny in the afternoon. One that seems suitable on a calm day may prove to be unsuitable when a strong wind is blowing. These changing conditions could not be observed or evaluated if the hive site was selected in an hour or so and on the basis of visits by only a few scouts. The long-drawn-out dancing debate provides time in which the hive site can be tested. A scout must not only find a place but be able to, in a sense, defend it against the criticisms and objections of other scouts.

Short of a filibuster in the United States Senate or some other parliament of man, there is nothing in the animal world quite like the debates staged by the dancing bees. For that matter, the entire system of communication which links together thousands of bees in a hive is unique. The languages of some other animals are more varied and flexible, but no other language can pass information between individuals quite so accurately as that of the bees. At the same time, few if any other animals are so dependent throughout their lives on their ability to communicate as are the honeybees.

PRISONERS OF BLIND INSTINCT?

Though the language of bees was only recently discovered and translated, some of the facts about the intricately organized life of these social insects have been known for many years. Extraordinary as the achievements of these animals are, we humans have a tendency to dismiss them a little impatiently and, it sometimes seems, even a little fearfully. The life of the bee is often used not to illustrate the marvelous things these little insects can accomplish through co-operation and communication, but rather as a horrible example of creatures who have lost their individuality. This argument runs: "Yes, the bees — very interesting, but they are prisoners of blind instinct. They have no choice." The comment is made in the same superior tone of a critical spectator who watches a magician's show and explains it away by saying, "It's all done with mirrors. It's not real."

This view that instinctive behavior is automatically inferior to the human way of doing things (the reasonable way) is and has always been widely held by men. It is a comforting theory since it assigns man a superior role, but it also limits our understanding and appreciation of the behavior of other creatures with whom we share the earth. More and more the accuracy of this notion is being challenged.

First, of course, it is impossible to compare behavior of two entirely different creatures with the aim of trying to prove one superior to the other. The dancing language of the bees would not serve as a method of communication among men, nor would our vocal system be of much use to the bees. In the end, about the only possible conclusion is that though bees and men have radically different societies and systems of communication, both species have survived (the bees longer than men) and there are vigorous populations of both today.

This is not to claim that the present state of things is necessarily perfect for bees, men, or any other creatures. Change is constant among all living things, though biological changes usually occur so slowly that we are not aware of them. However, there is no evidence that the direction of change, the purpose of evolution, is to transform such "low" creatures as bees, birds, or beavers into men. What might be called a tolerance of other than human methods of survival, a sense of respect and curiosity about other creatures, is essential for anyone who wishes to better understand not only the language but the behavior of animals.

An even more important criticism of the condescending theory that bees and other animals act according to "blind instinct" is the fact that the reality of "instinctive" behavior has become suspect. As was mentioned in the first chapter, the term "instinct" is one which scientists use very cautiously now. We have learned that language and other kinds of behavior are influenced by other than "instinctive" (inherited) factors. Many animals have been proved to observe their experiences, remember them, and adjust their actions according to what they have learned. This process is what has commonly been called intelligent behavior.

In the case of the bees, it appears to be true that inherited behavior patterns are very important, far more so than they are to men. The dancing bees do not learn to use their language as a human child does — to a great extent they are born with their ability to make their extraordinary signals and respond to those made by other bees. The bees cannot, except perhaps in a long evolutionary way, create new words for their language or rearrange the words in a grammatical fashion. Nevertheless, the individual bee is not totally dependent on her inheritance, not completely lacking in the ability to learn from her own individual experiences.

The tests of Von Frisch and many others clearly demonstrate that an individual bee can and does learn, that her experiences influence her language. Bees were easily taught to remember certain colors, shapes, and smells and associate them with food. They also learned to expect food at a certain time of day. Bees can, as has been described, adapt their language when obstacles or winds disrupt their routine. The ability *to adjust* may be instinctive, inherited, limited to a few alternatives, but the decision to adjust must be made by the individual bee on the basis of her observations and experience.

A complicated experiment which illustrates the learning ability of bees was performed by Martin Lindauer, who once transported a hive by air from Ceylon to Germany. After the journey the bees were released. They found that the sun was in a different position and appeared to be moving in a different direction in Northern Hemisphere Germany than in Ceylon. With their familiar sun compass apparently badly out of adjustment, the bees were confused in finding directions. However, in forty-three days these transplanted bees had learned to navigate according to the northern sun.

The common belief that bees operate only as a fixed part in the great machine of the hive is also not entirely true. There are maverick bees. Bees, apparently without any physical deformations, sometimes do not behave as do other members of the hive or do not follow the routine behavior pattern. For example, every now and then during one of the food-collecting dances a member of the "audience" who has followed the performance attentively will fly off in a different direction from that given in the message. There is reason to believe that this is done on purpose, but even if it is a mistake — a failure by the dancer to give good instructions or a failure on the part of the second bee to understand — the action demonstrates that a bee can behave differently from other bees.

As an alternative to common or conventional behavior, individualistic acts can be of great value to a species. The chances are that the bee who does not follow directions will not find as rich a source of food as the first scout described in her dance. However, there is a chance that the maverick will find something as good or better. Since the vast majority of bees will be doing the conventional thing, following the directions of the dance, the eccentric insect can be spared even if her efforts are completely wasted. In terms of the welfare of the hive as a whole, this individualistic behavior represents a sort of long-shot bet, which the colony can afford to take. Individualism, the difference in behavior of two creatures of the same kind facing similar circumstances, has been observed in many species of animals from bees to chimpanzees to men.

The view that similar animals react to their environment in very similar ways, according to machinelike principles and with machinelike consistency, is useful when it comes to describing the *general* behavior patterns of bees, monkeys, or men. But the mechanistic theory seems to be inadequate when it comes to understanding the behavior of particular animals. For centuries men who have worked closely with animals — not necessarily scientists and scholars, but herdsmen, hunters, trainers, field naturalists — have observed that there can be differences between animals of the same species. Sometimes these differences are overdramatized, as when an emotional owner claims to have a wonder horse or a genius dog. Nevertheless, the idea that animals have personalities is not sentimental but has been proved through many objective tests. Chimpanzees, one of the more intelligent animals, have been studied intensively in laboratories. In any test with a number of chimps, a kind of behavior which might be called typically chimpanzee will be disclosed, just as there will be an average grade if a classroom teacher marks a test according to a numerical curve. However, just as with students, there are few chimpanzees who will show completely average behavior; the performance of individuals will vary. Each will show personality differences.

Anyone interested in animal behavior and communication must recognize and take into account this mystery of individuality. It could be, for example, that more patient observation will show that among the bees there are good and bad dancers, bees who communicate more and less accurately than the average, just as there are some men who are moving orators and some who are silent and tongue-tied.

3
Sing and Show: Birds

Hawk

BIRDS ARE everywhere, and everywhere they are, they are vocal. Since they, like us, are noisy creatures and since our language is based on vocal signs, men have assumed for years that one of the principal activities of birds is communication. Poets, for example, have been particularly fascinated by bird calls. For centuries they have insisted that bird songs are hymns to beauty, love, freedom, happiness. Some of these translations have been taken with a grain of salt, poetic license being what it is, but the usual impression has been that the birds must be saying something. Since their style of vocalization was often so pleasant, it seemed natural to assume that what they were saying — the subject of their songs and calls — was probably pleasant, poetic, and imaginative.

Thus, when ornithologists began to make various discoveries about bird language — that, for example, chickadees make sixteen meaningful songs and calls, that chickens have a twenty-two-signal vocabulary — the information was not received with the same sort of astonishment which greeted announcements about other animal languages. It seemed that scientists were only proving what most people had believed all along — that birds do communicate.

Especially for the more poetically inclined, the real language of birds may have seemed less extraordinary than what it had been assumed to be. While it is true that some bird songs and calls seem to express feelings that might be compared to love and serenity, many of the most beautiful songs are apparently vocal reactions to such emotions as jealousy and hostility. Rather than expressing grand and beautiful "thoughts," most bird vocalizations deal with rather simple, commonplace subjects — hunger, alarm, identification. Furthermore, though birds are persistent communicators, their vocabularies, in comparison with other animals, are not extraordinarily large, nor do they express meaning with exceptional accuracy. No birds (and few other animals) are able to communicate such precise information as honeybees are able to do through their dances. When it comes to expressing individual emotions and moods, birds make fewer communicative signals (sounds and gestures) than do many mammals.

One of the reasons that birds have perhaps been overrated as communicators is that they appear to be more social, more involved with others of their kind, than they actually are. Birds often are seen in large flocks or colonies but often they congregate for reasons that have nothing to do with sociability — because a particular place offers good nesting sites or food supplies, for example. No birds have a social organization comparable to that of the bees, ants, and other social insects, where each member of the colony spends most of his energy contributing to the welfare of the group. The young of a few birds, penguins for example, are cared for co-operatively — any available adult feeding any hungry fledgling — but this behavior is neither as specialized nor as common as it is among social insects. Wolves, lions, certain whales co-operate in hunting; they herd quarry together, and sometimes arrange ambuscades. Occasionally a pair of falcons appear to help each other as they hunt, but this behavior is infrequently observed. Some birds, particularly those of the crow family, will mob common enemies. Some colonial nesting birds will as a group attack intruders, but common defense tactics are less frequent, less well organized, than among many insects and mammals.

One spring I was able to spend most of the daylight hours watching and photographing red-winged blackbirds in a small Michigan swamp. These birds give the outward appearance of being very social. About thirty pairs were nesting in this cattail bog. However, the longer I watched, the more impressed I was with how antisocial the birds were. They nested in small family groups of a single pair or several females and a male. Each family had its own territory, and between families most of their communication involved shouting threats at each other — "Get away, stay away." The males singing "oka-lee, oka-lee," the females with a variety of calls and pugnacious gestures, were intent on keeping their area clear of other blackbirds.

Occasionally a heron or a crow would cruise over the swamp. A male would give an agitated battle cry and rise to harass the intruder. Other males reacted to the alert call of the first, but did not come to his aid. Once the bigger bird had flown past the immediate airspace of the first, he would settle back down in the reeds, letting the other black-

Red-winged blackbirds and crow

birds deal with the foreigner as best they could.

All of this is not to say that birds are not communicative animals — they are, more so than many — but they are not such masters of language as men have sometimes assumed them to be. The fault clearly lies not with the birds, but with our own overactive imaginations.

From the standpoint of communication the birds are probably the most studied of any class of animals. The reasons for this are practical. Birds are not particularly secretive; the sounds and gestures they use are easy to observe; and they are common (there are eight hundred species of birds in North America). The accessibility of birds has made them a favorite of both professional scientists and thousands of amateur naturalists. Particularly during this century, an impressive amount of information has been collected about birds and their behavior — much of it related to their means of communication.

It has been found that the most communicative of the birds react to various situations with about twenty songs and calls. To these vocal signals must be added certain gestures and plumage displays which birds also use in their communication. All in all, the most communicative birds have a vocabulary of between thirty and forty vocal and visual signs.

There is no universal bird language. The sounds and signs vary from species to species, and there may even be "dialects" among members of the same species who are geographically separated. For example, house wrens in different parts of the United States have slightly different songs. "Dialects" are heard more frequently when birds are singing than when they are giving calls (single notes in reaction to some immediate happening). The reason seems to be that birds are born with the ability to make most of their call notes. Songs, on the other hand, are to a greater extent learned from adults. (Canary owners have discovered that young birds put within hearing of an adult develop into better, truer singers.)

While there is no standard set of signals which all birds can make and respond to, there is a certain similarity in subjects about which birds communicate. Thus, a male red-winged blackbird, perched on a swaying cattail, singing "oka-lee, oka-lee," sounds very different from a male mockingbird trilling in a clump of honeysuckle. Yet both, in different song languages, are saying much the same thing. They are announcing who they are, that they are in their own territory, and that other males trespass at their own risk. In the same way, a drake duck bobbing his head up and down in front of a hen and a tropical lyrebird displaying his magnificent tail plumage to a female are both intent on attracting and impressing a mate.

Many of the signals that make up the vocabulary of bird

language have something to do with alarm, identification, flight, feeding, territory, aggression (hostility toward birds of their own species), courtship, and mating. In the following pages a few examples are given of the kind of signs some birds make and respond to in these situations. Since the season of the year has great influence on the behavior of birds, and therefore on their communication, examples are arranged somewhat in calendar fashion.

ALARM SIGNALS

Almost every species of bird has a call expressing "Look out — danger." These calls are well developed and many birds have several different ones that distinguish between different sorts of dangers. The calls are among the most familiar to us because men are so frequently the objects which cause birds to give the danger signal. Danger calls can be heard in many different places and at all times of the year. Yet for me, when I think of danger calls, I think of those made by black-capped chickadees in the fall of the year, in a particular grove of scrub pine. The association is strong because I not only have heard the calls repeatedly but often depend on them for information.

In the autumn one of the world's great wildlife pageants is played along the sharp ridges of the Appalachian Mountains. It is then and there that the diurnal birds of prey, falcons, hawks, and occasionally eagles, are migrating from summer breeding grounds in the great northern forests to their winter ranges in South America, the Caribbean islands, and the southern parts of the United States. The Raptores follow the ridge, riding the updrafts which are created when strong northwest winds strike the mountainsides. Buoyantly, effortlessly, the birds of prey sail southward.

For more than a decade, I and a few friends have been going to the ridges in the fall to meet the migrating birds. We go to watch the spectacle, and also to trap and band hawks with rings of the United States Fish and Wildlife Service. We band the hawks partly because this serves as an excuse to go to the mountains in the fall, and also because the banding and the records submitted to Fish and Wildlife scientists help to increase the knowledge of the hawks, magnificent birds against whom too many men war cruelly and ignorantly.

Taking a wild, free hawk from the air is a thrilling experience which has been compared to fly-fishing in the sky. Hawks are lured down from the sky by a tethered pigeon. When a hawk has moved onto the decoy, a large net, held down by springs, is released by pulling a trigger line from

Hawk

a small brush-covered blind. The bownet (so called for its shape) flips up and over the hawk, who is then taken from the net, measured, banded, and released to resume his migratory journey.

One of the difficulties of this sort of trapping is restricted vision. Hawks have, perhaps, the best eyesight of any living creatures. Therefore the blind must be tight enough so that hawks cannot see in. This in turn means that the trappers have difficulty seeing out, the narrow window slots commanding only a small slice of sky. Since some hawks in their hunting dive will travel at more than a hundred miles an hour, they are often on the decoys before the hunter sees them and can get his lines ready.

In this situation some early-warning system is of obvious value. At the blind which we use in the mountains west of Harrisburg, Pennsylvania, we have such an automatic sentinel system provided by the chickadees. The blind is built in a small clump of Virginia pines, in which the black-caps always seem to be foraging. We have come to depend on these little birds to let us know when a hawk is approaching. Invariably, one of the chickadees will see the bird of prey while he is soaring above the small valley a half mile away, which our blind faces. The chickadees give a sharp, insistent danger call. This call is easily distinguishable from the one these birds give in response to danger which they discover on the ground, and much different from the alarm they give when they see a hawk trapper approaching the blind. The call of the first chickadee is taken up by the rest of the flock. The closer the hawk approaches, the sharper and more insistent are the calls of our sentinels.

When the hawk is close to the blind, even though we may not be able to see him, we are able to make a good guess at what species he is by "reading" the signs of the chickadees.

Red-tailed hawks are the species which most frequently come to our nets. They are large birds (sometimes their wingspread is nearly five feet), but relatively slow and clumsy. A red-tail has practically no chance of capturing a small, agile bird. The chickadees seem to realize this. They continue their warning call as the hawk approaches, and keep it up while he is over the pines, even when he is in the net. Occasionally, however, we are visited by an accipiter hawk. This group is represented by three species in the United States — sharp-shins, Cooper's hawks, and goshawks. All three are slim-bodied, quick, and very maneuverable. Their natural prey is birds, which they are well equipped to pursue and capture. When one of the accipiters approaches, the chickadees begin to call, but the alarm note is different. We can recognize more panic in the note. The certain sign to us that an accipiter is approaching is not a sound but the sudden lack of it. When the accipiter sweeps directly over the pine grove, the chickadees and other birds become abruptly silent and do not move or become vocal until the hawk has disappeared.

Of the birds I know, the crows have the largest repertoire of danger calls. Sometimes these big, intelligent birds act as sentinels when we are in the hawk blind, but since it is only coincidence that they are nearby when a hawk approaches, they are not as dependable as the chickadees who are always in the pine grove. To us, the hawk alarm call of a crow has always sounded like a harsh "hawk, hawk," but we have suspected that we were listening to our own imagination rather than the voice of the bird. Therefore in rereading Ernest Thompson Seton's chapter on crows in his book *Wild Animals I Have Known*, I was pleased that this famous naturalist also heard the crow alarm call for birds of prey as "hawk, hawk." Seton, a very keen observer of wildlife, identified five separate crow alarm

Crow alarm calls

Be on your guard

Danger

Great danger – a gun

Hawk, hawk

Great danger – a gun, a gun; scatter for your lives

calls. Seton's musical notation for these calls is shown on the facing page.

Each bird has different and distinct alarm calls, the squeak of a chickadee being much different from the rasping note of a crow. Nevertheless there is a certain similarity between the warning signals of many birds — a quality which again seems to me best described as panic. Whatever it is they have in common, birds respond to the alarm calls of others by making their own calls, dispersing, or hiding in silence. Near our blind, chickadees, crows, bluejays, titmice, flickers, and white-throated sparrows all obviously recognize each other's danger calls and react to them.

Not only other birds but mammals also have learned to benefit from this sentinel system of the birds. I have watched squirrels, rabbits, even deer, who seemed to recognize and react to alarmed birds. Many other hunters, trappers, and outdoorsmen, besides those who wait for hawks on mountain ridges, have made use of the alarm system of birds. By learning and listening to the calls of birds, a man can extend his knowledge of what is happening around him far beyond the range of what he can directly see and hear.

The question of motive, why the birds give the danger calls, is an interesting one. Ultimately, of course, there can be no final answer since we cannot know for certain what goes on in a bird's mind. However, outward evidence indicates that a bird does not give his alarm call with the intention of warning his companions, much less other animals who are eavesdropping. The bird, it seems, upon becoming alarmed, *reacts* by giving a distinctive call. He has no apparent, no heroic plan in mind, such as "I must warn the others." However, other birds recognize the alarm call and, in turn, *react* to it, by taking up the call themselves or fleeing, or hiding, depending upon the situation.

Regardless of motive and purpose, the result of alarm

calls is to pass highly useful information between the birds. In some respects this type of communication can be regarded as a valuable social service that the birds perform for themselves and many other animals, including hawk trappers.

IDENTIFICATION SIGNALS

Though there are a great number of alarm calls, that part of the birds' vocabulary is in many ways the easiest to learn and understand. Alarm calls are generally the same throughout the year, and they are given in response to a definite, easily identifiable situation. With other calls the cause and meaning is not so clear (for men, that is).

For example, a cardinal in the spring, whistling from the top of a spruce, is by this song announcing his nesting territory, throwing out a challenge to invaders, and seeking to impress his mate. He is also identifying himself, his location and mood. A young nestling, chirping in the nest, gaping with open mouth, is also identifying himself to his parents. There are many songs, calls, and gestures, which serve at least in part as a means for birds identifying themselves. Many of these signals are closely associated with courtship and nesting, and are described in the following sections dealing with these types of behavior. However, there is another set of commonly observed signals by which birds identify themselves, and which have little to do with the breeding cycle. These are the calls one often hears birds make while feeding and flying together in flocks.

The chickadees, feeding in the pines behind our Appalachian hawk blind, utter tiny, twittering noises as they forage through the pine groves. These sounds do not seem to communicate much specific information. Each bird twitters as he examines the tree trunk, but his calls do not seem to produce any definite reaction in the other birds. The meaning of these sounds seems to be rather a general one — "Here I am" — and they serve to keep the flock together. These small, feeding calls are given in sort of an offhand, involuntary manner, when the birds are busy and at ease. They might be compared to a man humming as he is engrossed in his work, almost unaware that he is making the sound. However, with the chickadees and other birds, these feeding calls also serve the purpose of assuring the flock that "all is well." As long as a bird hears the twittering call all around him, he has no cause for alarm. As soon as one bird becomes alert to possible danger, he gives a danger call, and all the birds break off the serene twittering.

Another good example of the same sort of communicative behavior can be heard among chickens in a barnyard. As they feed, they will make soft, absent-minded clucking noises. As soon as they are disturbed these are broken off and replaced by calls of excitement or alarm. Not all feeding "calls" are vocal. The rhythmic drumming of woodpeckers as they dig out insects from a tree trunk appears to pass along the information, "Here I am, all's well," to other birds.

Feeding calls can also communicate information about food and, when they do, indicate a sort of co-operative behavior on the part of the birds. Crows, again, have a very distinctive call, which brings others of the flock to the place where they are feeding. Gulls have a particular call, uttered when they have found an abundant source of food. Their call will bring other gulls from several miles away. Interestingly, if a gull has found only a scanty supply of food, he does not make the food call. The "come here" cry seems to be a reaction to the excitement of finding more food than he can consume.

Many other birds besides hawks migrate along the ridges during the autumn. In our blind we often see large flocks of swallows, purple grackles, robins, and geese. When the wind is right and these migrants are flying low enough, we can hear their flight calls. Each species has a distinctive call but the calls serve a similar purpose. Again the birds are calling, "Here I am," and the call serves to keep the flocks together, even when darkness or clouds restrict their vision.

There are also nonvocal flight identification signs. The sound produced by the wings of some birds is distinctive, serving to identify members of the flock and to keep them together. The wings of purple grackles make a distinctive whirring sound when they take to the air. Occasionally as we sit in our hawk blind, a large flock, several thousands of these birds, will light in the field. They will perch for a time, scattered throughout the thickets. Then, in alarm or restlessness, one bird or small group will rise, their wings whirring. Instantly, before they can possibly see the first birds, all the members of the flock respond and rise in flight.

There are also special flight gestures by which birds identify themselves to others of their kind. Konrad Lorenz, one of the most famous and most respected scientists who have studied animal behavior and communication, described these gestures as used among a colony of free-flying jackdaws that he established on the roof of his house. One fall a large flock of wild jackdaws settled down close by the house. The young birds in the colony that Lorenz had established joined the migratory birds and showed every indication of flying off with them. The colony was saved by the action of two adult males. These old birds would single out the youngsters of their colony, fly low over them, approaching from behind, and just as they were in front of the young birds, make a particular wobbling gesture with their tail. While doing this the old males made a distinctive sound, which Lorenz translates as "kiaw." The combined meaning of these vocal and visual signals was "Follow the leader – Fly with me." Eventually the old birds were able to bring back all except two of the young birds.

Signs which identify individual animals and keep large groups together are not restricted to the birds. Certain movements of schools of fish, the "flag display" of a white-tailed deer, the barks of dogs serve a similar purpose. However, because birds are so far-ranging and speedy, they are observed to make and respond to these identifying signs more frequently than most animals.

TERRITORIAL CALLS

Sometime in the last week of February a phoebe arrives in our yard and shortly thereafter begins to sing. For me, the phoebe's arrival and his song are the unofficial beginning of spring. From then on bird song, which has been conspicuous by its absence during the winter months, will serve as a musical background to all our outdoor activities.

The phoebe's song is related to the reproductive cycle, as is most of the bird language one hears and sees from early spring until late summer. During this period, it is very difficult to divide bird sounds and signs into neat, definite categories. However, simply for ease of understanding, the first songs of birds can be referred to as territorial – as long as it is remembered that other factors influence these "first territorial songs," and that territorial songs continue to be heard throughout the breeding and nesting period.

The first male phoebe takes up his position in a sycamore tree that shades a wooden bridge, underneath which a pair of these flycatchers have built a nest and raised a brood of

Phoebe

young each spring for the past five years. As the male sings, he is musically staking his claim to this nesting site. It cannot be said that his singing is directed toward any particular listener, for he sings simply in reaction to his inner mood and physical state. However, the result of the song is to pass along a considerable amount of information to other phoebes.

First, the song announces the sex and identity (each phoebe, each bird of any sort has an individual style which, though humans may not, other birds do recognize). The song also serves as a challenge or warning to other males. The territory is already spoken for, or sung for, and a second bird thinking about moving in will have to cope with the first. Finally, the song is in the nature of a self-advertisement aimed at females. In this respect the meaning might be translated as "eligible bachelor with good homesite wishes to make acquaintance of young lady, object matrimony." The early songs of many male birds serve the same purpose as that of the phoebe, to establish a territorial claim and to attract a mate into the territory.

COURTSHIP SIGNALS

One of the purposes of the early spring songs that we have called territorial is to bring pairs together. Therefore, these songs also are part of the courtship behavior of birds. (In the same way, courtship signals described in this section also serve to define the nesting territory of a pair of birds. It is difficult to describe animal behavior without dividing it into categories, but these divisions are artificial.) In an arbitrary way we might say that courtship and the use of courtship language begin after a male and female have come together in a possible nesting territory.

Courtship perhaps seems like a sentimental word to use in discussing animal behavior, but it accurately describes the activities of birds. Among many bird pairs, there is a period early in the reproductive cycle when they have not yet mated, but when the question of whether or not they will mate is decided. In this period, which might be called engagement, males seek to draw the attention of the hens and to impress their prospective partners.

For the male, courtship is a period of self-advertisement and, like all advertisers, he uses striking vocal and visual signals to state, or perhaps overstate, his case. Again, since we cannot truly know the inner life of an animal, it is impossible to determine exactly what qualities convince a hen that she should choose one cock in preference to another, or what points a cock tries to emphasize through courtship language. However, it appears from the human standpoint, that the males seek to make themselves seem as handsome, bold, and confident as possible. They accomplish this not only by vocal means, songs and calls, but also by exaggerated display gestures and postures.

One of the notable courters is the Australian lyrebird. The male is one of the finest songsters in the world. In his territory he clears little openings which serve as stages for his performances. During the midst of his courtship singing, one cock was observed by an ornithologist to sing for forty-three minutes, during which time he incorporated into his offering parts of the songs of at least twenty other birds. As he sings, the male puts on a magnificent visual demonstration, using his plumage to create an eye-catching (and mate-catching) advertisement. In the tail of the male are two large feathers which are lyre-shaped and give the bird its name. Normally the tail is carried flat, but in courtship displays it is held upright. The lyre feathers are spread and the softer plumage of the ornamental tail is thrown forward over the male's head like a veil. The original shape of the bird is disguised and he struts about his clearing as a great iridescent feathered fan from which comes a stream of song. Eventually, if a lyrebird has proved himself grand enough, eloquent enough, in the use of this language of courtship, his efforts will be successful, and a hen will be convinced to join him.

In many birds who are not songsters, courtship is carried on largely in a language of gesture display. A good description of such courtship behavior and communication is given by H. Albert Hochbaum, in his book *The Canvasback on a Prairie Marsh*. Male canvasback ducks use four distinctive courtship gestures which Hochbaum called the head throw, neck stretch, sneak, and threat. (See the illustration on the facing page.) A fifth courtship signal is a repetitive "coo" note uttered by the drakes.

Unmated canvasbacks hold "courtship parties" when they return to the northern marshes where they breed. These parties involve several drakes and one hen. The males swim about the hen, cooing, and repeatedly making one of the four courtship gestures. Together or separately, the drakes will rush at the hen, who may respond with the neck-stretch

Canvasbacks; courtship gestures

gesture and a clucking sound, but in general remains aloof. When all the drakes in a courtship group rush at a hen simultaneously, she may take to the air for a short flight, with the drakes in close pursuit. When she lands, the drakes will resume their courtship gestures.

The apparent purpose served by these courtship gestures is to give the drakes a chance to speak for themselves before a hen, and to permit the hen to judge between the competitors. When the hen makes her selection she stays close to one particular drake and clearly shows her preference for his company. Together the now-engaged pair will try to drive away the remaining drakes who have taken part in the courtship party. Soon the rejected males lose interest and go off to present their arguments to another hen.

The well-known "drumming" of grouse is another example of courtship communication (the drumming of the male also serves as a challenge and warning to other cocks). As the male drums, parading back and forth on a log, his feathers are raised, his whole body expanded. Again the objective (reaction, expressing his mood and condition) is apparently to make himself as impressive as possible. The creature to be impressed, the smaller, plainer hen, will in time hear and react to the booming sound, and come to join the strutting male.

Another curious tactic used by courting males as a signal to females that they are ready and willing to set up housekeeping is to build false nests. The male house wren, for example, will hurriedly construct crude nests in several locations. This behavior is apparently largely communicative, his way of asking, "Would you like to live here?" Once the female has mated, she usually ignores the nest site the courting male has found, and even when she does use a place he has selected she rebuilds the nest.

Hawks, who are among my favorite birds, are not exceptionally communicative as a rule. However, in courtship their language is magnificent. Pairs speak to each other by doing what hawks do best, flying. High in the air a pair of hawks wheel and circle in courtship play. The male performs fantastic aerial acrobatics, diving at his intended mate, stopping just inches short of collision. One spring day I watched Cooper's hawks courting. The two graceful birds gyrated above my head for nearly two hours without landing. They were saying to each other the same thing that all courting birds do: "Join me, be mine."

FAMILY SIGNALS

When courtship and mating are completed, nesting begins. For most birds this is the most social (and consequently communicative) season. Not all, but many mated birds stay together through the nesting period. Both males and females co-operate to care for, defend, and educate the young. The relationships between adults, between adults and young, between one family unit and others, create many situations where communication is necessary and is used by birds.

Throughout the nesting season, defense of a particular territory remains a prime concern for a pair of birds and the subject of a considerable amount of communication. During the early precourtship days, the male's chief interest is to lay claim to a territory and attract a female to it. Once nesting has commenced, both birds, but particularly the male, are occupied with defending this territory and the nest itself against intruders of all sorts.

Among the trespassers that nesting birds guard most vigilantly against are others of their own species. Some of this hostility seems to be based on the possessive this-is-mine attitude of a pair of birds toward their territory. However, the suspicion with which a pair regards others has a practical side. By protecting a territory, certain birds are also conserving their food supplies. Also egg breaking, destroying hatched young, and mate stealing are not unknown among some species of birds.

Among most pairs who stay together during the breeding season, the male is most active in guarding against and repelling intrusions of neighbors. After the nest has been completed his territorial song is somewhat different from that of the spring. Now it is almost entirely a no-trespassing announcement. As a general rule, most birds sing their territorial songs during the breeding season, perched near the center rather than at the boundaries of their home ground. The closer they are to their nesting site, the more aggressive and confident they seem to be.

I once watched two indigo buntings demonstrating this

kind of behavior and communication. Each had a nest (on which sat a hen) in thickets underneath a power line. The two nests were about two hundred yards apart, and the normal singing post of the males was on the power line above their nests. About equidistant between these two positions ran a line, invisible, but quite real for the buntings. This was the boundary between their territories. In their regular positions the two bright blue males would alternately bombard each other with bursts of song, the meaning of which was, "Here I am. This is mine. Keep out."

Occasionally one bird would begin to edge along the wire toward the territory of his neighbor. When this happened, the singing of the bird being invaded became even more excited and aggressive. ("Stay out. I mean it, I mean it. This is your last warning.") At the same time, the further the invading bird advanced away from the center of his own domain, the less confident he appeared. (Among most birds, being close to their nest gives them courage, or perhaps more incentive to be aggressive.) Not only to me, eavesdropping below, but to the two birds involved, their relative position in regard to the center of their territories was clearly indicated by this game of vocal "hot and cold."

In most cases the warning alone was enough to repel invasion. But sometimes communication was not enough. If the intruder hesitantly entered his neighbor's property, the home bird flew at him, enraged. Invariably the trespasser retreated, though a few minutes later if his neighbor entered his territory he would be the pursuer and the other bird would flee.

Defense of territory is particularly important for birds such as gulls, who nest in large, thickly populated colonies. The Dutch scientist Niko Tinbergen, in his book *The Herring Gull's World,* described many territorial squabbles. Though the herring gulls have several calls which they use to challenge intruders, certain distinctive gestures seem to be more important as signals to warn off other gulls. Two peculiar ones Tinbergen has called the grass-pulling and choking signs. The first is used between two males. When they confront each other one will bend down and pluck at grass or moss. His opponent may repeat the gesture. Tinbergen, one of the most accurate of observers, believes this gesture expresses aggression and is recognized as such by other gulls. Grass-pulling only takes place on the boundary dividing territories. Like the buntings and many other birds, the closer to his nest the more aggressive a gull is, and conversely, the farther a gull trespasses into a neighbor's territory, the less confident, the more ready to retreat he is. The choking gesture, also indicating aggression and warning toward invaders, is used by both male and female when together they oppose the entry of a stranger into their territory. Both birds lower their heads, open their mouths, and appear to choke. Peculiar as this gesture appears, it is effective. Confronted by a pair of angry, choking gulls, intruders usually retreat.

Though as a rule colonial nesting birds appear to have more difficulties with their neighbors than those with larger territories, sometimes close neighbors will, in response to a call, help the victim of an invasion. Among the jackdaws observed by Konrad Lorenz this was the case. Jackdaws nest in cavities and have a particular note, "zick-zick" according to Lorenz, with which they defend their nesting hole. When one pair is invaded by another member of the colony, the "zick-zick" changes to "yip-yip," which apparently has the meaning of "Get out at once, this is very serious." If the intruder does not retreat, the yipping becomes louder and it brings all the nearby jackdaws of the colony to the invaded nest, all yipping. They are apparently reacting to the call of the beleaguered pair, not com-

Herring gulls; the choking sign

ing with the intention of driving away the intruders; but this is the result. In the turmoil that follows, the original invader may himself begin to call "yip-yip." Shortly all the birds retire, justice has triumphed, and peace is restored.

The language, songs, calls, and gestures by which birds defend their territories and nests against others serve two basic ends. First, the challenges and warnings actually deter invasion. Secondly, by using language, birds are usually able to defend their property without fighting. If they were unable to express their mood and intention with vocal and visual signs, their only recourse when invaded would be to attack the intruder. Especially among the larger, better-equipped birds, constant battling could have serious and bloody consequences.

Birds must also defend their nests and young against truly foreign invaders, all manner of creatures who may be far more dangerous than other birds of the same species. To meet this need an entirely different set of signals are necessary from those used to warn or frighten their own kind. (The choking gesture may deter another herring gull but clearly would have the opposite effect on a fox.) As anyone knows who has stumbled on a bird's nest, the birds do have a sort of universal warning language, a series of signs and gestures by which they express hostility, alarm, anxiety, and distress.

The first purpose of these signals is to discourage or frighten the invader. The warning calls of a bird defending its nest are as easy to recognize as the hiss of a cat or the growl of a dog. Supposedly docile pigeons have a particularly effective signal in this respect. Disturbed on her nest, a pigeon gives a rumbling warning which not only communicates the same information as a dog's growl ("Beware, I'll attack") but sounds remarkably like a growl.

Another method of protecting the family is used by many birds, but is particularly well developed in certain ground-nesting species such as the killdeer. The female will behave as though she is crippled, dragging a wing, hopping away from her young, luring the intruder after her. This reaction must certainly be classified as communicative, since the whole purpose of the pantomime is, through gesture, to trick, to misinform.

The various defensive calls and gestures used by birds also serve as alarm or distress calls, and bring assistance to the calling bird. With most birds the only aid they can expect is from their own mates. However, among colonial nesting birds like Tinbergen's herring gulls, Lorenz's jackdaws, and others, members of the colony will react to these alarms or predator calls and come to the defense of the pair being molested.

After the eggs hatch, the young birds become part of the family communication system, responding to signals of the adults and making signals to which adults respond. Some of the language ability of young birds is innate, possessed from the moment they hatch, but other communicative behavior is learned. Thus, young red-winged blackbirds, for a few days after they are hatched, will rise up and trustingly open their mouths to be fed when a human taps their nest. They will do this even though the parent birds are making alarm calls, even attacking the intruders. A week later the same young, on hearing the warning calls, will immediately react by crouching down in the nest and remaining motionless.

Young Gallinaceae (chickenlike birds) learn to respond quickly to a variety of warning calls. They have need to because, unlike songbirds, these youngsters are active almost from hatching, scurrying about after their mother on the ground. Mother grouse, pheasants, quail, ducks, geese, and others can make commands to "freeze," "flatten," "scatter," "hide," "come," which the chicks obey.

For most birds, the first calls the young themselves give are, understandably, concerned with food. Very early, nestling birds begin uttering plaintive food calls and making begging gestures (the most common being to rise and open their mouths) the meaning of which is clearly "feed me, feed me." These signs have considerable value to young birds. Often the most forceful and effective pleaders are the survivors in a crowded nest, where competition between nestlings is real and serious.

Many young birds, after they have left the nest, make distress calls which are somewhat like their food-begging calls. Bluejays are particularly zealous parents and continue to feed and guard the young for several weeks after they have left the nest. During this period the adult jays respond quickly and ferociously to distress cries of their young. In years of handling and training large birds of prey, I have never been more than scratched, but I once received a painful scalp wound from a bluejay whose fledgling I incautiously approached.

As the breeding season progresses, many young birds separate from the adults as soon as they can fly. Other youngsters stay with the adults and receive a certain amount of schooling, especially instruction in communication. Crows particularly seem to drill young birds to respond to the signals of their rather large vocabulary.

Konrad Lorenz has written that young jackdaws seem to be taught through language. He noticed that young, inexperienced birds would trustingly allow predators, even a cat, to approach them. However, after an adult jackdaw had swooped down, uttering a "rattling" warning call, the young birds would from then on regard cats as dangerous. The reaction of young jackdaws to the rattling signal is innate, but in this case they learned what caused the warning, recognized that a cat was danger, because they were told as much by an adult.

As the young begin to develop their ability to use and understand signals of this kind, the cycle of bird language is completed.

Obviously bird language has evolved so that birds can communicate between themselves. Nevertheless, men have always been fascinated with this language and have persistently tried to establish some sort of communication with birds. The mutual interest that birds and men have occasionally shown in each other's language, and the success they have had in communication, are largely based on the fact that we and the birds have comparable vocal abilities. No matter how well we may understand or admire the dance language of the bees, for example, it is virtually impossible for us to make the kind of sign that will enable us to communicate with these insects. With the birds it is different. Difference of mentality and behavior aside, we make and are accustomed to the same sort of signals. Mechanically at least, the vocal parts of our two languages have much in common.

With a little practice, almost anyone can "speak" a few words of one of the easy bird languages. For example, one can duplicate a variety of crow calls – alarm, danger, "come here" – and predictably draw a certain response. Birds, accustomed to receiving information through vocal signs, can also be taught to respond to human voice signals. Crows are particularly talented along these lines. A tame fish crow, who spent a summer with us, would come to a food whistle and would also come to be stroked when his name, "Barry," was called. Hawks, neither the most intelligent nor communicative birds, when trained for falconry, will return to the falconer's glove in response to a whistle.

Hunters have long made use of bird languages, being able to attract many game birds by duplicating their calls. Naturalists also use bird language in their ornithological studies. Konrad Lorenz, for example, would "speak" to ducks and geese in order to control and instruct birds with whom he was working. Many bird watchers learn a few words of a bird language to bring birds closer for study or pleasure. Bird language has also been used for the opposite purpose – to drive away unwanted species. For example, one of the most effective means of discouraging flocks of starlings from roosting in city buildings has been to play a recording of a starling "danger – fly away" call.

Finally, there is the matter of mimicking, a talent with which birds have impressed men through the centuries. Nearly everyone has heard members of the parrot or crow families who can imitate the human voice with great accuracy. However, not so many realize that a "talking" parrot or myna bird is demonstrating an ability which many birds possess. Dozens of songbirds in North America – jays,

Parrots

catbirds, mockingbirds, thrushes, crows, etc. — naturally imitate the songs and calls of other birds, mammal cries, music they hear from radios or phonographs.

Why birds mimic remains a mystery. Since the study of animals became scientific, the tendency among biologists has been to explain behavior in terms of its survival value, to show how a particular action now or once contributed to the welfare of a species. The survival value of many of the signals by which birds communicate is relatively easy to see. Alarm, territorial, courtship, distress, feeding, warning sounds and gestures all are (or once were) of obvious utility.

The usefulness of mimicry is, however, far from clear. Various theories have been advanced: that birds mimic to divert attention from themselves; to drive away the birds they are mimicking; to attract prey; or to increase their individuality by incorporating strange bits of song into their own. None of these explanations is entirely satisfactory and attempts to show the survival value of mimicry lead to some very complicated and shaky conclusions.

However, one matter does seem clear in regard to birds who are able to mimic humans. They do not associate meaning with the words as we do, nor use them to carry on reasonable communication. No talking bird has ever been known to recognize the words of his vocabulary or to express his own meaning or mood through words.

The mystery about motives which cause birds to mimic other creatures, and the purpose that mimicking serves, perhaps has considerable bearing on our over-all understanding of animal behavior. Certainly the poets who translated bird song into love sonnets went too far in sentimentalizing birds. On the other hand, perhaps we have gone too far to the other extreme. By insisting that all animal actions must have practical, survival value, we have perhaps needlessly and inaccurately "scientized" animals. Certainly there are many points in common between human and animal behavior, and much human behavior seems far removed from the immediate problem of survival.

For example, we whistle a tune as we work, or listen to a record or a concert, principally because we take pleasure in the sound. It is not inconceivable that a bird sings a song he has heard, or says "Polly wants a cracker," for much the same reason, because it amuses him and entertains him. It may even be that pleasure has some survival value for animals. It seems to have for humans. Perhaps we are making a mistake in insisting that individualistic, unpredictable, just-for-the-fun-of-it behavior belongs only to man.

4
The Long Conversation: Dogs

German shepherd

MAN'S ASSOCIATION with most domestic animals — horses, cattle, sheep, chickens — began as that of master and captured slave. With dogs it was probably different. Dogs entered into a voluntary partnership with men, and the chances are that it was the dogs who made the first overtures, who showed men that the association could be practical and beneficial for both parties. The ancestors of our modern dogs were for the most part jackal-like creatures who probably followed as scavengers after tribes of primitive men. The jackals followed at first for food scraps but may well have learned in time that they would get more to eat if they helped the hunting men — showed them where game was, cornered it, even held it at bay. In turn, men learned how useful these animals were not only in hunting but as sentries around the camp. The next step probably was for men to encourage these useful animals to stay around camp to be on hand for the hunt and to serve as guards. Men must have begun to feed the jackals intentionally, to adopt puppies, and eventually to breed their own dogs.

All of this is of course guesswork, because the association between men and dogs began long before recorded history (there have been domesticated dogs for at least ten thousand years). Yet on the basis of what the partnership is today, it seems quite clear that it was formed and has endured because men and dogs have a unique ability to communicate with each other.

Wolves, jackals, coyotes, foxes today live as the ancestors of their domestic cousins must have lived thousands of years ago. Judging from observation of these wild members of the canine family, the first dogs must have possessed a language which was peculiarly adaptable for communication with man. Like the language of men, the language of dogs is made up chiefly of vocal signals, gestures, and facial expressions. Also, dogs, like men, are very social animals, living and (of great importance) hunting together in more or less permanent groups. Before they joined the camp of primitive hunters, the first dogs were accustomed to expressing themselves to their companions by means of signs and had the habit of recognizing and responding to signs other dogs made. This background simplified the problem, for both men and dogs, of developing a meaningful system of communication.

Once the partnership was formed, men unquestionably sought to improve on the dog's natural talent for communication by training individual dogs and, more importantly, through selective breeding. When we speak of an "intelligent" or "good" dog, we generally mean one who is especially responsive to humans, has exceptional talent for understanding what we expect of him and for making himself understood to us — a good communicator. Through the centuries this special sort of responsiveness has been desirable in hunting, working, and companion dogs. Good (communicative) dogs have naturally been kept and prized for breeding.

This process of selective breeding, coupled with the fact that men and dogs have learned a good deal more than they once knew about each other, has created a unique situation in regard to communication. Dogs are now the only animals which communicate more easily with another species — man — than they do with their own kind. Quite simply, the sign vocabulary which men and dogs customarily use is usually larger, more informative, than that which is used between dogs. For example, "fetch" is a simple command which a man can teach almost any dog. Yet no dog is able to give a signal to which another dog will respond by fetching. There are many other commands, requests, gestures of affection and disapproval used between dogs and men which are not used between dogs.

A domestic dog uses, in a sense, two languages. He exchanges information with other dogs and expresses himself to man by using the sound signs and gestures of "old dog" — the language of reaction. He largely inherits the ability to make and comprehend the signals of this natural language. However, when it comes to understanding humans, a dog must *learn and remember* the signs that a man uses to express himself. "Sit" is a common sound signal given by men to their dogs. Almost any dog can learn the meaning of this signal, but there is no dog who understands the meaning of the word unless it is taught to him. Dogs do not inherit the ability to understand any particular human sign, but they do seem to be born (and again, selective breeding may be an explanation) with an undefinable sort of eagerness to respond to men. Dogs seem far more anxious to learn how to communicate with their human companions than they do with other dogs. This sets the domestic dog apart from all other animals, even his wild relatives, and largely explains the enduring partnership and friendship between men and dogs.

The four German shepherd puppies whose first days and efforts at communication were described in the opening chapter were born about the same time as the idea for this book. As the book progressed, these young dogs provided a firsthand opportunity (as this sentence is being written, one of the pups is asleep under the desk) to observe how dogs use their own language of reaction and learn to communicate with humans. Furthermore, during the puppies' first few months there was a rare opportunity to compare

Freya's puppies

their language behavior with that of wild dogs and in a sense with that of the wild ancestors of domestic dogs: often to their dismay, the four pups had as a companion a red fox vixen of about their own age.

Before going further with the story of the vixen, who was named Sylva, and the four pups, it should be noted that a fox is not ideally suited as a subject for making comparisons between wild and domestic dog behavior and language. While dogs and foxes are both members of the family Canidae, they are distant cousins within the family. Foxes do not interbreed with dogs as will wolves and jackals. Also, though foxes are highly intelligent, they are among the least social of the dogs. Adult animals do not hunt together in packs as do, for example, the wolves. A mated pair of foxes or a mother and cubs may range together in certain seasons, but for the most part their hunting behavior more closely resembles that of the solitary cats than that of the more gregarious dogs. From the standpoint of communication it would have been more interesting to have raised a wolf (there is a little wolf blood in some breeds of domestic dogs) with the puppies. However, wolves are hard to come by in the Appalachian Mountains, while Sylva was born in a den only a few miles from our house. Despite the many differences, she and the pups had enough in common to make the experiment practical and the comparisons interesting.

Sylva was bought from a bounty hunter who had dug her, two sisters, and a brother from their den. Her purchase price was slightly more than what he would have received if he had turned in part of her hide to the Pennsylvania Game Commission. At the time of her capture she was probably about a month old, two weeks older than the puppies. Sylva was not much bigger than a small house cat but she was every ounce a wild animal. She spat and hissed, catlike, and when approached, cowered in the corner of her cage. Her tiny teeth were sharp and numerous, as we soon learned.

Despite her first unfriendly reaction, taming Sylva was neither a long nor a difficult process. She was after all a very young animal who needed both care and companionship which only we could provide for her. She was installed in a large cage in the kitchen where she was exposed to the normal comings and goings of the family. In less than a week she seemed to have decided that while the sight, sound, and smell of humans was unquestionably strange, they were not necessarily dangerous. She remained cautious, quick to flee if startled, but she was no longer perpetually terrified, nor were her reactions savage.

We soon began to let her out of her cage in the evening when the house was quiet. With the delicate tread so typical of the fox, she pranced about the floor as if each step were being taken on the thinnest of ice. Within two nights she had thoroughly explored the ground floor of the house. She quickly learned where the butter dish was kept, how to jump on a chair, not to be alarmed at the sound of the electric pump, where to find escape and hiding "holes" under the refrigerator and in the cupboards. She also learned to come up to a person sitting quietly in a chair, take food from his hand and allow herself to be stroked gently. Only once after her first days of terror did she bite seriously. That was when a visitor, after announcing confidently that he had "a way with animals," tried to pick her up by the scruff of her neck. He held the vixen only as long as it took to get her teeth out of his wrist.

At six weeks, if our calculations as to her birthdate were correct, Sylva had a vocabulary of about ten sounds and signs. These were distinct signals which she used repeatedly in response to certain situations and which expressed something about her mood or intentions. (There were surely other signs which we did not understand.) Fright and hostility were expressed in several ways — flattened ears, tail depressed between her legs, and a low humming growl which unmistakably meant "hands off." When she was excited, as when she was anticipating her food, she gave a sharp little "yap-yap" bark which one hears adult foxes making in the wild. Her tail was a good instrument for measuring her confidence. If it was held high, like a plume, it meant she was secure, engrossed in her own affairs. The more alarmed she became the lower it dropped. At night, after Sylva had had her run, she was herded back in her cage, the door locked, the kitchen lights turned off, and she was left alone. She squalled and screamed at first in pure anger. Then she began to whine, the whine rising to a shrill screech something like that of a cat whose tail has been stepped on. This was a cry of loneliness, made only when

Sylva

she thought she had been deserted. It stopped if someone came downstairs, turned on the lights, and talked to her.

Sylva also began to make efforts to communicate with us, to develop and comprehend signs that a wild fox would never use. Each time she was fed we made a particular whistling call-note and within a week Sylva was responding to the whistle, coming even when food was not offered. She also learned to sit up and "beg" for food. At first she would only do this when we actually held a piece of meat in our hand. Her reaction was simply to jump up, trying to reach it. Within two weeks, however, she would come to us and stand up on her hind legs, as a gesture (a symbol) indicating that she wanted to be fed.

While Sylva was exploring her world and developing her vocabulary, her future playmates, the four puppies on the back porch, were doing little except growing. In comparison with the fox they were much slower to develop physically, less alert sensually to their world. They also had considerably less to "say." Protected, guarded by their mother, they had little to fear, no warning "hands off" sound or signal. They would cry and whimper when lost or hungry but in general their responses were less numerous and less specific than the signs Sylva made. When Freya or one of the family came onto the porch they would come to the visitor in greeting, providing they didn't fall over their own feet on the way. However, as far as coming in answer to a specific signal, as Sylva did to the whistle, this was beyond them. Sitting up and begging was a gesture that they would not make until they were almost three months old. They were too fat to adopt this posture, they were still being nursed and had no reason to make it, and mentally they could not master such complicated behavior or communication.

The prospect of introducing the fox to the dogs intrigued

but worried us. We anticipated no difficulty between Sylva and the pups. Young animals usually get along well before they begin to acquire hunting, killing, and escaping habits. Sylva was obviously too quick and alert for the pups to harm even in play and they were too fat and well padded for her to damage. Freya, however, was a different matter. She was jealous of her pups even when old friends among the other household animals came near them. She had, for example, chased a visiting male beagle onto and (eventually) through the roof of a large outdoor aviary. Furthermore we recalled only too well that two springs before, Freya and another dog had killed two young foxes.

As a first step in bringing the dog cousins together we moved Sylva's cage outside into the yard where the dogs were now spending their days. The pups at first paid little attention, but Freya walked over to investigate. Sylva's reaction to Freya was immediate and explosive. She flattened out on the bottom of the cage, wriggled, swished her tail furiously while trying to press her nose through the screen to touch the big dog. All the while she emitted an eerie, wailing sound, such as we had never heard her make before. In general she seemed to be expressing the strongest sort of joyful excitement. It is impossible to know what goes on in an animal's mind but we had the strong feeling that Sylva was not acting as she did, not trying to reach Freya because she regarded the dog as a substitute for her mother. Rather, her excitement seemed to spring from meeting another of her own kind. She had been polite with us, occasionally, shyly, sought our companionship, but we were clearly not her kin. The little fox's ecstasy at meeting the big dog reminded us of that of a foreign traveler who unexpectedly meets someone from his home. "Here," Sylva seemed to be saying, "is someone of my own kind."

Freya's reaction to Sylva was much more subdued. She

was curious and puzzled. (A perplexed dog shows his mood in much the same way a man does. He turns his head to one side, wrinkles the skin on his forehead, frowns. It is a standard expression among dogs the world over.) Since Freya did not show open hostility and with Sylva hysterical in her eagerness to join the dogs, we decided that whatever was going to happen to the vixen we would not keep her caged any longer. In any circumstances, caging a wild animal seems a pointless activity. It is impossible to enjoy or truly observe a confined animal. With an active, affectionate animal like Sylva, being locked up was a particularly frustrating experience, not only for her, but also for the person who did the locking.

That evening, after the dogs had been put away, the door of her cage was opened, never to be shut again except on her very last night with us. Half an hour later I stepped out of the kitchen door and whistled. Out of the dark from under a privet hedge came Sylva, stepping high like a soldier on parade, her tail carried proudly like a banner. Quite naturally, she came into the kitchen, sat up for a bit of meat. After she had eaten she pranced back outside and curled up in her open cage. Sometime that night she changed quarters. The next morning when called she appeared from under a large boxwood bush where she had dug out a shallow pit. This bush and hole served as her den and retreat for the rest of the summer.

The following morning, Freya with her puppies tumbling along behind came into the yard. Sylva streaked out from under the boxwood, dashed wildly at Freya. As we watched tensely, the little fox ran in circles around the dog, once jumping right over her back. She nipped at Freya, rubbed against her, and all the time continued the strange wailing call we had heard the day before. Freya backed off, still puzzled, but she did not on this first encounter or later make any attempt to attack the vixen. Freya continued to regard the fox as something different from her own puppies, but something that could be tolerated if not loved. Thus it was that our mixed fox-dog pack was established.

For the next seven weeks, Sylva and the dogs provided a continuous opportunity for observing the habits and outlook of both wild and domestic canines. Since the six animals were seldom apart, communication figured importantly in their behavior. As the vixen and the pups became more practiced at expressing themselves and comprehending their companions, we, who watched from the sidelines, were given a good course in elementary dog language.

The pups and Sylva spent much of their time playing. There was one basic sign which indicated their intention to play — which served in a sense as an invitation. The pup (or fox) would crouch down, with his forelegs extended. He would rest his head on his paws. He would lash his tail furiously. From this position he would spring toward the intended playmate and a tumbling sort of wrestling match

Sylva and pup

would begin. The pups and Sylva not only made this sign but responded to it when it was made by another. When one of the young animals came on another in the "let's play" position, they would either crouch themselves or else brace themselves for the charge that was sure to follow.

From the very first, Freya was very obviously Sylva's favorite among the dogs. Sylva played tirelessly with the pups but she treated them with what can only be called contempt, as if they were her inferiors, as they were in quickness and keenness. Toward Freya, Sylva showed the unreserved admiration of a younger sister for an older one. Sylva was forever trying to get Freya to play with her, but she was seldom successful. Freya was of course an older animal, a mother with responsibilities, and simply less playful than the fox. Also Sylva used the wrong "language" when she asked Freya to play.

In many ways Sylva and the dogs were like a French-speaking man trying to communicate with a Spanish speaker. With the dogs and fox, their "root" language was the same, "old" or original canine, as Latin is the root language of both French and Spanish. But just as French and Spanish have evolved through the centuries, so have "domestic dog" and "fox." The signs and signals have been modified, the meanings subtly changed.

To invite Freya to play, Sylva would first take up the crouch position. Then she would launch herself toward Freya and very purposefully nip the dog at the tip of her muzzle. Then she would draw back as though asking Freya to chase her, and when the dog did not, Sylva would repeat the nip. This is a gesture that domestic dogs use, but it has a different meaning for them from the one "let's play" that Sylva obviously intended. A pup will nuzzle against his mother's muzzle, sometimes even chew on it a little. Adult dogs of the same sex will also nuzzle each other in this way, but the definite nipping sign among dogs is normally only made by an adult female, directed toward an adult male. It is a kind of flirting gesture, expressing affection as much as anything else. The previous winter Freya had gamboled around the big eighty-pound male who was the father of the pups and she had nipped at his muzzle just as Sylva did at hers.

In foxes this sign clearly had a different meaning than it did with dogs. It was probably a play sign used between pups and adults (Sylva never nipped at the pups in this way, nor did they use the gesture with Freya) or perhaps between adults of the same sex. In any event, both animals were frustrated by their failure to communicate. Freya looked puzzled, as much as if to say, "What in the world is this crazy fox trying to say — why doesn't she speak dog?" Sylva continued her nipping and her wail rose higher as Freya did not respond. Usually these meetings ended with Freya retreating in disgust.

Along with gestures and postures which invited play, the young dogs had signs by which they indicated they wanted to break off play. When things became too rough for a pup he would lie down on his side or turn over on his back, often raising his legs. Prone, he would wag his tail apologetically, perhaps whimper. A pup in this position was the picture of complete helplessness and this was exactly the meaning of this sign — it was a gesture of surrender: "I quit — don't hurt me." Once a pup assumed this position, his attacker might continue to nose him, but he would stop tormenting his victim and soon wander off looking for another playmate.

With the puppies Sylva seldom used this surrender gesture, since she was invariably the one to whom surrender was made. By August the pups weighed twelve pounds or so, but though the little vixen was only a third their size, she was more than their master in catch-as-catch-can play. One of her favorite tricks was to lope slowly before a pup, swishing her bushy tail. When she had thus lured one of the little dogs away from his companions she would turn, pounce, and knock him off his feet. After a few rounds of this game the pup would give up, roll over on his back. Sylva might stand over him for a few moments triumphantly, as if to make sure he had truly surrendered, but she would not continue to maul him.

Occasionally when a pup seemed to be getting much the worst of his encounter with the vixen, Freya would come to his aid. She would stand menacingly over Sylva, legs stiff, tail high and waving slowly. Sylva had no trouble understanding this sign, which means "beware" in dog language the world over. In response, Sylva would make her own surrender gesture, which was slightly different from that of the pups, but similar enough for Freya to understand. Sylva would flatten out on the ground, extend her hind legs, wag her tail ingratiatingly, and emit the peculiar wailing note with which she had first greeted Freya. (Apparently in fox this cry is used to express "I mean no harm" as well as "I think you're wonderful.") Just as Sylva did with the pups, Freya would sometimes lean down and touch the apologetic fox with her nose. In this position she could easily have killed the vixen with one snap, but she always respected the truce-and-apology sign.

There is a particular surrender sign which the male pups, but not their sister or Sylva, later developed. Meeting an adult male dog, pups will often try to play with him. If the adult is in a good humor he will permit this roughhouse up to a point. However, if the youngsters try his patience too severely he will make a warning growl, or may even roll them over on their backs and hold them down with his paw. This usually occurs only between adult males and young males since all female dogs, even puppies, are usually able to tease adult males with impunity. When a young male puppy is disciplined he will not only roll over on his back in the surrender position but will also often urinate, losing control of himself out of nervous alarm. The reaction is involuntary but it serves a purpose. The odor released seems to reassure the adult male that he is dealing with a young whippersnapper, who may deserve to be disciplined, but is not a serious rival.

Failure to understand this behavior and the surrender gesture often leads to exasperating (and also amusing) difficulties between young male puppies and their human owners. One reason that dogs have adjusted so easily to the partnership with man is that they seem to regard their owner in somewhat the same way they once regarded (and wild dogs still do) the old male who acted as pack leader. A young dog is inclined to show the same respect and willingness to surrender to a human as he does to an adult male dog. Therefore, when a puppy is disciplined by scolding or slapping, say in some disagreement over housebreaking, he is very apt to roll on his back and repeat the accident which started the trouble. According to the logic and language of dogs he is acting perfectly properly, showing both his respect and his submissiveness. The best rule to follow in punishing a young male puppy is to do it outside.

From the early surrender gestures that puppies use in play grows a complicated system of communication through which members of the dog family keep the peace between each other. Dogs make and respond to a large number of somewhat related signs, the purpose of which is to establish rank and status. This part of their language has certainly had a high survival value for the canines. Though we think of our own pets as docile creatures, we must remember that the dogs are hot-tempered, hunting animals, among the largest and best equipped of the predators. They are quite capable of killing large animals, including members of their own kind. In dog society many situations arise which generate hostility — rivalry over food, mates, and territory. Given their formidable fighting abilities, pride, and uncertain tempers, it is obvious that some system of social restraint is necessary if dogs are to live and hunt together without constant bloodshed.

Law and order among dogs is based on a rigid caste system. In a group of canines, each member will have a certain rank which determines how he will treat other dogs and how they will respond to him. A lower-ranking dog may challenge a higher-ranking one, but except under extreme provocation, the challenge will not result in a fight. The higher dog will react by making certain signals, gestures, and sounds which announce, "explain," his rank. Once this is understood, the lower dog will usually withdraw his challenge and submit to the animal with greater status. As long as a dog "knows his place," he will get along peaceably with his companions.

Age and sex are factors which automatically affect a dog's status. Puppies, as has been said, are largely immune from serious attacks by older dogs. A pup's surrender behavior serves to show that he belongs to this privileged age group. Young dogs continue to defer to their elders for several years and as a rule behave and are treated as second-class citizens, standing back while older dogs eat, giving up sleeping spots, following behind when dogs are hunting, and in general acting with respect and caution. Male dogs, as a rule, will never fight seriously with females, though females will sometimes turn savagely on males. In wolf packs, a female often takes on the same rank as her mate (wolves mate for life). If he is of a high caste, a pack leader, his mate is treated with considerable respect.

The real difficulties in determining rank among dogs are between adult animals of the same sex, particularly among males. When a young dog reaches maturity or when strange dogs meet, some fighting may be necessary to determine rank. (The basis of canine caste systems is something of a mystery. Often rank appears to be based purely on size and fighting qualities. However, sometimes experience and "cleverness" seem to be factors. Often a much larger, stronger dog will follow and defer to a more experienced but weaker animal. Packs of wild and domestic dogs, including adult males, will sometimes have old females as their leaders. About the best that can be said is that somehow, among themselves, dogs determine who is the "best" dog.) Once rank is established, dogs seldom have to fight to keep their places. Communication, the signs by which they announce their status, serves as a substitute for warfare.

Among the dogs, perhaps the most complicated "status language" has evolved in the wolf pack. Wolves are not only among the most social of dogs, they are also the strongest and fiercest. Therefore they have considerable opportunity and need for this type of language. By facial expression, position of the tail, and other communicative gestures, a wolf meeting another indicates whether his status is superior, inferior, or equal to that of the second animal. Because this information can be communicated by signs, there is seldom need to settle the matter of respective rank by battling.

The caste system and language of domestic dogs are similar to those of the wolves but not quite as well developed. (It would perhaps be more accurate to say that this behavior has been modified and some of the status vocabulary lost. The pack organization is not so important among domestic dogs as it once was, nor do they normally have the opportunity and need for developing social relationships with many other dogs.) Still, men dealing with several dogs find it useful to learn some of the canine "status" language. If, for example, when two dogs meet, one makes signs indicating superiority and confidence (tail erect, eyes wide, head cocked) while the other shows submissive signs (ears and tail depressed, hind quarters lowered) there is little chance they will fight, no matter how ferocious their growling may sound. Left alone, the lower dog will probably defer to the higher-ranking one. If, however, two strange dogs both display aggressive, superior signs, and neither is willing to back down, they may fight to settle the matter of rank.

The whole matter of dog manners and language was much on our mind in regard to the future of Sylva and the four puppies. As youngsters, Sylva held the upper hand, but within a few months the pups were going to be five or six times her size. The question would then be whether these very different dog cousins had learned to understand each other well enough to restrain their natural aggressive instincts. Would Sylva be treated as a small female dog by her grown playmates or would they one day decide she was simply a curious wild animal to be hunted? The question was never answered. Unexpectedly, the dog-fox pack was broken up, and although at the time it seemed a tragedy, it may have been in the long run a fortunate thing.

Before the coming of either the pups or the fox a family vacation trip to Michigan had been scheduled. When the time came a variety of arrangements were made for the many animals who were in residence in and about the house. In the case of the canine corps, two of the puppies were sent to new homes. Two, both males, Dain and Durin, were kept and, along with Freya, were to be taken to Michigan. It seemed neither practical nor kind to take Sylva on such a trip and as an imperfect compromise it was decided to leave her with a young friend. However, since he lives on a farm with such things as chickens and strange dogs, Sylva would have to be caged until we returned. The night before we left she was lured into a large cage. It was an unpleasant experience, making one feel like a sneak and a traitor. Sylva did nothing to relieve these feelings of guilt. Finding herself trapped, she began to howl and tear at the screen in panic. Sadly the cage was loaded into a truck, the plan being to deliver her to the farm the next morning. However, when morning came, Sylva was gone, having been able to tear loose a staple and the wire. We delayed our departure a day, looking and calling for her, but she did not return after her terrifying experience with the cage. Though we left word with neighbors about her disappearance, we never saw or heard of Sylva again.

When we returned in the fall with the dog pack cut in half, the two remaining pups, Dain and Durin, were big strapping thirty-pounders and seemed to be growing at a visible rate. Though they still deferred to Freya, they no

Wolves

longer needed her to supply food and did not seek her out for protection. Together they began to explore the world on their own, roaming through the woods, swimming in the creek, learning that squirrels were fun to chase, skunks were not, and other useful things.

Later in the fall, this exploring led the dogs to decide on what was their territory — their home range. Fortunately the bounds they set for themselves more or less corresponded with our property lines. They began to indicate the frontier of their "country" in the traditional manner of dogs, by marking certain trees, fence posts, and rocks with the scent of their urine. The messages they left were apparently as clear to other dogs as the "No Hunting" signs I posted were to hunters. It sometimes seemed the dogs' signs were obeyed better than mine were.

A big, black, male shepherd dog lives about a half mile from our house. Several times I saw Dain and Durin encounter this dog on "neutral" ground, along the highway. Both pups cringed before the older dog and he took their surrender as a matter of course. Once, however, I saw him wander into the pups' territory, after having first "read" the scent messages which they had left on the trunk of a sycamore tree. When the pups found the stranger, they both charged him. Anywhere else he would have answered with a growl, a series of superior gestures which would have quickly ended the pups' impertinence, but now he responded differently. He wagged his tail in a friendly, almost apologetic fashion and then began a dignified but unmistakable retreat. The reason for his sudden change in behavior was not that Dain and Durin had suddenly found courage. It was that they were home. Territorial factors change rank among dogs. A dog at home is king, even though he may hold very low rank elsewhere. The black shepherd had read the signs on the sycamore tree and the meaning of this message was supplemented by the pups' signs of aggression. He understood he was trespassing and retreated without loss of face.

Another matter that the two pups quickly settled was their own rank. Much to our surprise, it turned out that Durin was the top dog. His brother, Dain, is a handsome, golden-colored animal, bigger and stronger than the grayish Durin. Dain was more at ease with strangers, challenging their entry onto the property, while Durin tended to be timid in this regard. However, between the two dogs, Durin clearly had the higher rank. At feeding time or when they got ready to lie down, Durin took precedence and Dain deferred. There is a narrow footbridge which crosses the creek, only wide enough for one dog. If the dogs start to enter the bridge at the same time, Durin draws himself up in a cocky "get out of the way" stance, while Dain makes slight surrender signs, backs off as if to say, "Excuse me, after you."

So far as we know, the dogs established their caste system without fighting. As is usually the case with dogs, once the matter was settled they remained good friends. However, since they are still young dogs, very evenly matched, their personalities changing, there still may come a time when only a real battle will serve to establish status. (This, Durin the smaller dog outranking his bigger brother, may be a case of brains over brawn. During the past months it has become increasingly clear that Durin learns more quickly and easily than does Dain.)

The ability to bark develops rather late in dogs and this sound is never much used in "intimate" conversations between them. Rather, the bark is their bugle and horn, a signal to be used in battle and chase. In October, Dain and Durin found their barking voices. By midwinter they had six easily recognizable barking calls, each of which signified they were engaged in a certain kind of activity. There were barks to challenge other dogs, challenge strange humans, greet members of the family; barks indicating they were chasing a wild animal such as a raccoon, teasing one of the other domestic animals such as the nanny goat, or playing between themselves.

One dog did not give a particular kind of bark to inform the other; he barked in reaction to a given situation. However, the call served the purpose of communication. If Durin, for example, was howling a greeting to a member of the family who had arrived in the driveway, Dain would shortly appear, galloping directly to the drive, obviously ready to play rather than to challenge a stranger.

The wolves, those aristocrats of the canine family, have developed a very effective system of howling calls. In a general way the wolf calls serve to keep the pack together, inform members as to the whereabouts of their packmates. This is particularly useful since wolves hunt over large ranges. Farley Mowat, a Canadian naturalist who for a time lived in the midst of a family of wild wolves, noted that they seemed to know from the distant howling of another wolf, who he was, where he was, what and in what direction he was hunting. On one occasion an Eskimo companion who was a specialist in wolf language went off to prepare for a reindeer hunt after listening to the "singing" of distant wolves. Asked to translate, he said that the wolves he and Mowat heard were announcing the approach of a migrating reindeer herd. However, the wolves howling had not actually seen the deer; they simply were repeating the message given by wolves even further away, out of earshot.

As Dain and Durin were developing, by being exposed to new experiences, their innate ability to use dog language, to react to certain situations by producing certain signs and sounds, they were also *learning* the second language of domestic dogs — the signs of men. They barked in a certain way when on the trail of a raccoon because hundreds of generations of their ancestors barked in that way. They had to learn, however, to sit in response to the command, "sit." They had no inborn reaction to this vocal signal.

Among the first and most important lessons in communication the pups learned was that when we patted them, roughed their ears affectionately, said such things as "good boy," we were pleased with their behavior. In contrast, when we pushed them away, said "no" or "bad dog" in a certain stern tone of voice, they were in disfavor. Getting these pleasure and displeasure signals straight is the A B C of dog education. Because of their breeding and natures, dogs, unlike many other animals, are best trained by administering *intangible* rewards and punishments. The reward is praise and affection and the punishment is to withhold praise and express displeasure. Giving real rewards (food) and punishment (pain) can also be used but it is an awkward, ineffective system. Most people find it inconvenient to carry a pocketful of meat with them as bribes to get their dog to obey. As to physical punishment, this works fairly well as a means of teaching a dog *not to do something,* not to snatch food from the table, but it is a poor way to teach a dog *to do something,* to respond to a "come here" command. Normally, being whipped confuses rather than clarifies instructions for a dog.

Nearly every normal dog will work hard simply to please his owner (the ancestral pack leader). If a man has sense enough to translate his wants into signs a dog can understand, the dog will go to great lengths not to displease him. Seldom are the signs of pleasure and displeasure to which dogs respond formal ones in the sense that the command "heel" is. Dogs are geniuses at recognizing the emotional moods of humans from very small signs, signs which often other people cannot translate. A good dog understands a good owner not because he is bribed or beaten to do so, but because he wants very much to do so.

The first formal sign Dain and Durin responded to was a whistle which meant "come." At first they connected the whistle with food, since it was given at their dinnertime, but shortly they came in answer whenever it was used, not necessarily to be fed. The second formal sign was more complicated, more difficult for them to learn, and consequently won them considerable praise when they had mastered it. The two pups were to be "outside" dogs, and a shed in the barn was cleaned out and equipped with an old mattress for their use. The shed also was the place in which the dogs were shut up when their presence outside was inconvenient, as for example when a picnic lunch was spread on the grass. At first it was not much easier to get the pups into their shed than it would have been to have driven wild horses. Yet after a week or two, they would respond to the command "come" by walking voluntarily if not eagerly into the shed. Being shut up was the last thing these two exuberant young animals wanted, but they permitted us to do so as a way of being rewarded with our praise.

In December, when the pups were about six months old, we commenced spending fifteen minutes a day in formal obedience training with each dog. Ideally it is best to wait until dogs are older for this work (many trainers do not accept dogs who are less than a year old). However, we thought we would see what could be done, and if the training seemed to be too difficult for the pups we could suspend it until they were older. One reason for sending Dain and Durin to school prematurely was that they were such large, spirited animals, some restraint was necessary if they were to continue to have free run of the premises. This is probably the best and most common reason for training any dog. There is no real evidence that a trained, mannerly dog is any happier than a rambunctious, undisciplined one. What is important is that the more civilized a dog's behavior the more he will be allowed in civilized company and the more affection and attention he will receive.

Being observing creatures who want to please, all dogs who are around people learn something about obedience. However, there is a formal obedience course for dogs, which in this country has been developed and standardized through the American Kennel Club. It is quite possible to design a private curriculum for a dog, using a training sequence and signals different from those of the Kennel Club. However, the standard course and methods are suited to most owners and most dogs. Group obedience classes are sponsored by many local dog clubs. Also, since obedience training is neither mysterious nor difficult (patience on the part of the owner is the only secret), a dog owner can study any of several good books on the subject and give obedience instruction at home.

Obedience work, if the owner does not become a fanatic on the subject, is time well spent. Not only does it tend to make the dog more socially acceptable, it teaches the owner a great deal about the psychology of dogs in general and of his own dog in particular. Furthermore, since obedience training is nothing more than developing a vocabulary of signals by which man and dog can exchange information, this kind of instruction provides an ideal opportunity for observing and experimenting with animal communication.

As this is being written, Dain and Durin have been enrolled in their private obedience school for about four months. Free of the training leash, each dog now responds more or less dependably to the commands "heel," "sit," "stand," "stay," "down," and "here." They also recognize these same commands when expressed by hand signals. Though teaching both the vocal and visual signals slows down the training process somewhat, in my case it is useful since the dogs are often in the woods with me and there are occasions when I want to communicate with them without making noise.

In addition to the signals they both understand, Durin (much the quicker pupil) has begun a course in retrieving. Now, on the command "get the paper," he picks up the rolled newspaper which is delivered at the end of the lane and carries it to the kitchen door. After he has handed over the bundle he fairly swaggers with pride. Big Dain looks on a little wistfully as his brother is praised, but as yet the idea of picking up and carrying is not clear to him. It is probably just as well, since only one newspaper a day is delivered.

Considering their age and free style of living, the pups' progress has been satisfactory, but they cannot be considered exceptional in this matter of comprehension and communication. A completely trained obedience dog will, for example, recognize, remember, and react to about sixty hand and voice signals. Obedience training is normally reserved for pet and companion dogs. Other dogs who have more practical jobs learn different, perhaps even more complicated, sign vocabularies. Hunting dogs, retrievers, pointers, trail packs, hunt because it is their nature to hunt, but they modify their habits to suit the needs of man, learning complicated, "unnatural" responses to a variety of hand and voice signals. Dogs trained to serve as guides and companions for the blind learn to respond to more signals and to a greater extent than other dogs; they must also learn to give signals which pass along information to their owners.

To me the most impressive working dogs are the herders — collies and shepherds — particularly those trained to handle sheep. Working in obedience to hand signals these dogs not only keep a flock of sheep moving in order, but can divide the flock, cut out individual animals, deposit them in different pens, hold sheep, deliver them singly or in groups to the shepherd. It is a matter of opinion, but for me there is better communication between an experienced shepherd and his dog than there is between man and any other animal.

As we marvel at the comprehension and responsiveness of trained dogs we should remember that training does not alter the nature of dogs or create their special talents; it only modifies or emphasizes abilities which dogs naturally possess. Counterparts of the reactions of trained dogs can be seen in the behavior and language of wild dogs. Herding behavior has been observed in wolves — deer are driven and weak animals are cut from the herd. Because this involves "strategy" and co-operation, the wolves must make and respond to signs, just as do a shepherd and a dog. Many obedience training commands are aimed at getting the dog to take or hold a certain position in regard to his companion, "heel," "stay," "sit," etc. Here, too, naturalists have observed similar behavior in wolves and coyotes who hunt in groups. One animal will station himself in a hidden position and wait (stay, sit) while others drive game toward the ambush. In the same way, retrieving and pointing behavior is found in wild dogs. In guarding, an age-old service dogs have performed, men have simply found a way to make use of and direct the strong territorial sense of dogs. Trained dogs have unquestionably learned new tricks, but they can only learn them because a certain aptitude for this behavior has been inherited from the wild dogs who were their ancestors.

Every so often "wonder" dogs are discovered, exhibited, and written about. The wonder of these animals is that they appear to comprehend and use human language as humans do. A stock trick for these dogs is to give answers to simple arithmetic problems. For example, the owner asks, "How much is two and two?" Fido begins to bark, once, twice, three, four times, then stops and is praised.

What has happened is that the dog has been trained to begin barking at the command, "How much?" As he barks he watches his owner intently. At the proper moment the owner gives some small sign — a smile, nod, gesture — and at this signal the dog stops. Often the owners are perfectly sincere. They do not know they have made the telltale sign, nor realize that it is they who are doing the counting. They truthfully believe they have a reasoning animal, rather than an animal who is extremely talented at discovering the reaction his owner wants him to make.

It is difficult to divide behavior into separate categories, but in a general way it is accurate to say that ease of communication is fundamental to the enduring partnership between men and dogs. Other animals are more intelligent than dogs (apes, monkeys, elephants, whales, raccoons). Other animals could perform various services better than dogs (potentially a bear would make a better guard, a tiger a better stalker, a mink a better trailer, a crow a better sentinel). But as yet we have found no other animal whom we can so easily comprehend or communicate with as the dog. Very simply, we and dogs are working partners and friends because for centuries we have been able to carry on a long, meaningful, useful conversation.

5
If They Could Only Talk: Apes

Gorilla

IN THE fifth century before Christ, an admiral of Carthage named Hanno sailed off to explore the west coast of Africa. Among many other wonders, Hanno reported the following: "Having sailed by those streams of fire we arrived at a bay called the Southern Horn, at the bottom of which lay an island like the former having a lake and in the lake another island, full of savage people, the greater part of whom were women and whose bodies were hairy and whom our interpreter called Gorillae. Though we pursued the men we could not seize any of them, but all fled from us, escaping over the precipices and defending themselves with stones. Their women were, however, taken but they attacked their conductors with their teeth and hands and could not be prevailed upon to accompany them. Having killed them we flayed them and brought their skins with us to Carthage."

Since the time of Hanno and probably before, men have wondered about the manlike-but-not-men character and habits of the great apes. (Also, as in the case of Hanno, human curiosity has too often resulted in the apes being skinned.) Though we now know something more of the apes than the Carthaginian explorer did, our curiosity has not lessened. For example, whenever you visit a large zoo you will probably find the largest crowds gathered around the orangutans, chimpanzees, or gorillas. There is also a good chance of hearing in such a group some spectator say, "They seem so human. If they could only talk."

This remark, or ones much like it, may be almost as old as man's interest in the apes and yet it comes close to summarizing the findings of modern scientists who have spent years studying wild and captive apes. The similarities between apes and men have been found to be, if anything, more numerous and greater than they appear to be to the casual zoo visitor. In physique and physical abilities, as well as in many of their mental and emotional characteristics, the apes not only seem to be close to man, but closer to him than they are to any of what we men rather arrogantly call the "lower" animals.

Nevertheless, one great difference which intrigues both the zoo crowd and scientists specializing in the study of the apes is that of language. This is a great gap, perhaps the greatest, which separates the apes and men. While the apes, being intelligent, social animals, have a useful and relatively complicated language of their own, it appears to be much closer to that of birds, dogs, cats, than to that of men. The language of the apes is primarily a tool for communicating immediate information about things and events which are in and of the present. It is made up of signs which, for the most part, are made in response to the apes' immediate situation or observations. As yet there is little evidence that the apes have much talent for either creating or using abstract symbols to communicate, for "talking" about the past that once was and the future that might be.

Before considering how much, if at all, apes can talk to men, there is another matter of more importance, at least to the apes — how they communicate among themselves. A fine, exciting account not only of communication but of the home life of wild apes has been given by George Schaller, an American zoologist who for more than a year lived close to gorillas in the African Congo and studied these animals at closer range than anyone has before or since.

Schaller found that the gorillas were social animals, living in small permanent groups numbering from five to about thirty animals. While these groups served for the mutual protection of their members, the gorillas have few natural enemies, and the adult animals seemed to stay together for the sake of companionship as much as any other reason. In many respects the gorilla groups resembled primitive human tribes. In each of these tribes there seemed to Schaller to be a "head man," an old male who led as the animals moved about. The other animals, it appeared, did not follow the leader out of fear but more out of respect. They seemed to desire his company. Below the leading male in rank were other adult males, females, and juvenile and infant apes. Though each animal had his place in the tribe there was very little quarreling, few signs that lesser gorillas resented those with higher rank or sought to rebel against them. Older animals sometimes disciplined unruly or playful youngsters but both adult males and females were also seen to show concern for the welfare of infants and to assist mothers with their young.

There were a few solitary "hermit" gorillas, but for the most part the animals spent their time in close association with others. Therefore it is not surprising to find that they had the ability and need to communicate with each other. Schaller, in his book *The Mountain Gorilla,* has drawn up what amounts to a dictionary for the gorilla tribes which he studied. He was able to distinguish twenty-two sounds of communication. Some of these vocal signs described by Schaller are: a purr, which showed that all was well and the animal content; short, low-pitched grunts by which one animal indicated his position to others of the tribe, saying, in effect, "I am here"; a "waw-waw" sound that was used as a warning; a soft whine that served as a distress call and brought the attention of other members of the tribe; a chuckle given in play; a harsh "u-u-u" grunt by which males apparently ordered quarreling females to stop their bickering; loud, high-pitched screams which were warnings of great danger.

Gorilla family

These sounds represent a fairly large vocabulary but not a very precise one. Generally, it seemed to Schaller, the main function of the sound signs given by a gorilla was to catch the attention of the tribe. The sounds were often followed by some gesture or facial expression, which among the gorillas seemed to be the system of communication most used and the one by which they could pass along information most accurately.

Like all of the apes, gorillas have very mobile, expressive facial features. Their "looks," more than sounds, indicate how they feel — playful, peaceful, angry, impatient, afraid, curious. The famous chest-beating display of gorillas, the Tarzan trademark, seems to be a gesture of communication. Depending upon the situation, Schaller decided, chest beating might signify annoyance, alarm, or a sort of bluff directed at other gorillas. A peculiar, stiff-legged walk used by the leading male gorillas also seemed to serve a communicative purpose. When the chief took this posture and walked away it was clearly a sign, if not an order, to the others of the tribe to "follow me."

Another curious gesture was used by individual gorillas when they were startled by Schaller's appearance. They would stand still and shake their heads back and forth, sometimes letting their mouths fall open as they did. Schaller translated this as meaning, "Peace, I intend no harm." The scientist himself took to using this gesture when he came upon a gorilla unexpectedly. Standing in the forest, shaking his head, making the "peace" sign, Schaller could be said to have been "talking" with gorillas in their own language.

The important part that gestures and visual signs play in the language of apes has also been observed in colonies of captive chimpanzees. Like the gorilla, chimpanzees have a range of expressive sounds, but they seem to make more use of signs in communicating with each other. Even more than gorillas, chimpanzees have expressive faces, perhaps the most mobile features of any animal in the world. For scientists working with groups of chimpanzees the ability to read their emotions by the faces they make is not only interesting, but a very practical skill. A chimpanzee who looks angry is very likely to take some hostile action. If he has a playful face he is ready to play; a sulky animal wears a sulky expression. Since chimpanzees are accustomed to observing and judging the meaning of facial expressions in their own kind, they are alert and sensitive to human expressions. An angry, displeased look will subdue or even frighten a chimpanzee, and chimps who are laughed at appear to be humiliated, seeming to understand that they are being regarded with something less than respect.

Robert M. Yerkes, an American scientist who was a pioneer in the studies of the apes, would offer tests in his laboratories to two chimpanzees, the problem being such that its solution would require co-operation between the two animals. For example, the two animals might be given a box, too heavy for either one to move alone. It was observed that gestures were the form of communication used as the chimps tried to work out the details of their partnership. One animal would make a begging, asking motion to the other, requesting help. Or one might draw the other to the box and then by a kind of pantomime indicate what he wanted his companion to do.

Another interesting example both of a chimpanzee's use of signs and of his ability to learn took place in the Yerkes laboratory. A male chimp apparently had a sore mouth. His keeper asked him by gesture to open up, which he did. The examination was made but the trouble was not found. The man moved away, but the chimpanzee pulled him back, opened his mouth again, and pointed with his

Chimpanzees

finger to a small hard spot near the back of the jaw which was the source of his pain. The animal was clearly indicating, "It hurts here, Doctor," and did so because he had learned to expect care and attention from the man.

Because it is so like the gesture a man might make in the same situation, the behavior of the chimpanzee with the swollen jaw may seem at first to be very "un-animal." Actually, this gesture as well as the other signs and sounds by which the apes communicate is made in response to some tangible happening or condition — pain, for example. Dogs have been known to do much the same thing, pushing their master's hand to or away from a painful spot. Though these gestures can communicate information just as accurately as human words might, they are part of the language of reaction and used quite differently from the way men use their language.

As an example, the same information expressed by the gorilla's head-shaking gesture can be communicated by dogs and men. As we have seen, a young dog may do this by rolling on his back in the surrender position. A man can do it with the words, "I mean no harm." Each method is equally effective when used between members of the same species. However, the dog and chimpanzee can only use this sign in response to a very specific, immediate happening, meeting a stranger who puzzles and somewhat alarms them. Neither has any way of modifying this sign or using it to build a different kind of meaning. A gorilla cannot go back to his tribe and explain that he met a creature who intended no harm or upon seeing the man again explain to his companions that no harm will result. Without the encounter, the gorilla does not make this sign.

Though it remains largely a language of reaction, the apes, in comparison with other animals, have a very flexible and expressive method of communication. If these animals looked and behaved like dogs, cats, or horses, we humans would probably remark on how well they were able to communicate and let the matter drop. However, the apes do not look so much "animal" as they do "human" and their behavior often seems to match their looks. Therefore there is always the suspicion that these manlike animals may indeed talk to each other as men do, or, if not, perhaps might learn to use language as we do. It is a possibility which has intrigued not only the general public but scientists, who have collected considerable information about how manlike the apes really are. It is in fact only by recognizing the similarities in other areas that we can fully appreciate the dramatic way in which language separates men from apes.

The most obvious similarity between men and apes is physical. Our bodies and features look something alike and we use them in similar ways. Both have a remarkable ability for manipulating objects with the hands (and feet in the case of the apes). Apes and men are among the very few animals who use tools. Both apes and men can walk upright, though apes do not do so as easily as men. Apes and men suffer from many of the same diseases and they have similar diets. (In the wild, apes appear to be almost entirely vegetarians, as men probably were long ago. But in captivity apes learn to eat and enjoy meat.) The senses of apes, the way in which they know their world, are comparable to those of men. However, one important difference should be mentioned since it apparently has great bearing on the question of communication. Men and apes seem to have about equal faculties for hearing and seeing. However, the apes appear to give far more weight and pay more attention to what they *see,* in comparison with what they *hear,* than men do. Some observers believe that this difference can be traced back to communication. Because of speech, men have developed through practice their power of discriminating between various sounds to a greater degree than apes have. Apes, on the other hand, are perhaps a bit more sensitive to gestures, visual expression, and signs than we are.

The emotional life of the apes also shows a resemblance to that of men. Young chimpanzees (the apes who have been most carefully observed in special collections and laboratories) give and need affection. They are pleased with attention but can have temper tantrums when they have been denied a treat or disciplined. Chimps are quick to anger but can also produce something which resembles a laugh. Chimpanzees do not cry as we do because their tear glands are poorly developed, but they show unmistakable signs of grief when a friend dies or pity when a companion is sick or injured.

There are many instances of apes showing signs of jealousy and loyalty both toward their own kind and toward humans with whom they have close ties. An example of this kind of loyalty is described by Heinrich Oberjohann, who spent many years collecting African animals, especially monkeys, for European zoos. At one time he kept a large pen of mandrills, a large, ferocious forest baboon. A tame chimpanzee, Cozo, helped Oberjohann watch over the mandrills and sometimes would recapture escaped animals. Cozo and his distant baboon cousins had a great dislike for each other. One day when Oberjohann entered the mandrill cage to save a young animal being attacked by the adults, he himself was attacked. Cozo, the chimpanzee, leaped into the cage to assist his friend. Though more than a match for one mandrill, he was overpowered by a troop of these big monkeys and was killed before Oberjohann could rescue him.

Chimpanzees, and it seems the other apes, are creatures of many moods which they express easily. They have their ups and downs as humans do, but in general they seem to have what we would call happy dispositions. Neither in the wild nor in captivity do the apes appear to suffer greatly from what we would call emotional problems. Robert Yerkes, perhaps the outstanding American authority on the behavior of chimpanzees, believes that it is in this area, emotional balance, that men may have the most to learn from the well-adjusted chimpanzee.

The mentality of apes (and again, chimpanzees have been the animals most often used in laboratories) has been studied closely. Apes seem to learn rather easily, can reason to some degree, and in general act with intelligence in many situations. It is difficult to compare the mentality of apes with that of men because so many different skills are part of what we rather loosely call intelligence. In some tests chimpanzees perform almost as well as adult humans, but in others they do not equal the scores of very young children. Chimps, for example, have excellent memories, certainly one important factor in intelligent behavior. In one memory test, bits of banana were placed under one can of sixteen pairs of cans. Two monkeys, two chimpanzees, nine humans (four children and five adults) watched the arrangement of the cans and then were directed to select the one can of the pair that contained the fruit. The monkeys showed the poorest memory in this test. The chimpanzees scored better than the children and almost as well as the adults, some of whom were animal psychologists.

Other tests and observations have shown that chimpanzees, like children, learn both by imitation and by trial and error. In one laboratory, for example, a push-button-type drinking fountain was installed in the chimpanzee enclosure. As soon as one of the apes discovered how to operate the fountain, all the others learned the trick immediately, by imitation. Many observations have been made of chimpanzees learning through trial and error. If a box containing a tempting bit of food is locked with a simple catch, a chimp's first effort may be to break open the container. If he is unsuccessful in this attempt, he may begin to explore and fumble with the box until by accident he finds the way to work the lock. Once he has done this he will master similar locks almost immediately, showing that he has learned by experience.

Unfastening a simple catch may not appear to be brilliant behavior, but it should be remembered that many animals have great difficulty grasping the idea that if one approach doesn't work, another can be tried. A bird or a fish, for example, can be caught in a funnel trap, a box with a long tapering opening. Once in the pen a bird or fish will try to escape directly through the mesh of the cage, rather than finding his way back through the opening. When they do accidentally find the indirect opening, they do not seem to benefit by the experience. Caught again in a similar trap they will repeat their performance of trying to break free through the screen rather than seeking out the hole.

Some of the tests have shown that chimpanzees may use imagination to solve problems, that is, “visualizing” what would happen if they acted in a certain manner. Yerkes writes of a six-year-old chimp, Mammo, who was presented with a long box open at both ends, in which a banana had been placed. The banana was too far from either end of the box for Mammo to reach it with her hands. However, she had also been given a long stick. After a few unsuccessful attempts to reach the fruit, Mammo withdrew. Suddenly she picked up the stick and shoved it into the box, pushing the banana out of the other end. While this may have been only a lucky trial-and-error success, it appeared to observers to be an example of an ape using imagination and insight.

Other chimpanzees have learned to “work” for poker chips and use these tokens as we would coins to “buy” food. Another example of chimpanzee imagination was provided by a young ape named Vicki, of whom more will be said shortly. Vicki was raised like a human child in a hu-

Mammo

man home. Like a child she was fond of toys, particularly pull toys. One day she astounded her mistress by appearing, pulling an imaginary toy. Vicki carried this pantomime game so far as to get the make-believe string of the nonexistent toy wound around a real pipe. She complained until her mistress came and untangled the invisible cord. Such examples of imaginative, perceptive behavior have not been observed frequently, considering how carefully these animals have been studied and tested. In general, it is in this area of dealing with "unreal," intangible things and ideas that the apes seem most different from man. In many tests apes have proved very slow — in comparison with men — or apparently unable to understand underlying principles (the why and how of things) and cause-and-effect patterns (what happens if), and to visualize alternatives (suppose this were different).

This apparent difference between the way an ape's mind works and the way a man's does is probably the root reason for apes not using language as men do. The language of the chimpanzee (and that of other animals) is tied to real things and real situations. Thus the chimpanzee with the sore tooth pointed to the source of pain. A man might have used the same gesture but he could under different circumstances (speaking to a dentist on the telephone) have communicated the same information by words — symbols which had no direct connection with the toothache. "Tooth" and many other words in our language represent real objects or situations, but many other words do not. For example such words as *and, or, when, why, this, that,* are abstract symbols representing intangible arrangements or situations. We cannot point to an "and," as we can to a tooth, but we deal quite easily with the meaning of the word, understanding that it represents a connection between two things. This connection, which seems simple to us, is difficult or impossible for a chimpanzee to deal with since it is not something that can be seen, heard, or felt. Because the idea of *and* strains an animal's understanding, the word symbol — the sound "and" representing this abstract idea — is probably meaningless to him.

While it seems that the inability of a chimpanzee to juggle the thousands of abstract symbols which we use in our language is the reason he cannot communicate as we do, it is very difficult to be certain about what does or does not go on in the mind of any creature. Even when men study the inner life of other men, conclusions about mentality are hard to draw and often controversial. When it comes to trying to discover how a member of another species, such as a chimpanzee, thinks, the difficulties and chances of error are far greater. With this in mind some scientists have suggested that perhaps lack of ability is not the complete answer to this question of apes and language. There remains the possibility that apes might have the ability to master at least a simplified version of human language, but have not shown this ability because they have no motive or opportunity to do so. As a far-fetched example of a comparable situation, we might consider primitive men living at the equator who do not have snowshoes. They lack these tools because there is no reason to have them. If they were transplanted to the Arctic they might be inspired by necessity or imitation to invent and use these tools.

Animal psychologists have wondered if chimpanzees do not use language for the same reasons tropical tribes do not use snowshoes. Perhaps, it has been suggested, the best way to discover what, if any, language talents an ape had would be to raise a young animal as a human child in a human family, where language is an all-important tool. In such an environment a young ape would have the same reason and opportunity for using language as a human child. To answer these questions about language ability and others involving the development of apes and men, several infant chimpanzees have been "adopted" by human families. One of the most patient and important of these experiments was carried on by Keith and Cathy Hayes, who brought an infant chimpanzee, Vicki, into their home and gave her the same care and attention that a human baby would receive. Keith Hayes was a scientist working at the Yerkes laboratory where Vicki was born, but it was Mrs. Hayes who was with the little ape constantly and who described Vicki's first years in a book, *The Ape in Our House.*

Vicki came to the Hayeses as a three-day-old infant. At first she lay relatively helpless in her crib, swaddled in diapers. However, her physical and mental powers began to develop at an earlier age and a faster rate than is normal for a human baby. At three months she had learned to pull a string to get food and at four months she was walking and climbing about the Hayeses' apartment with great agility. (The story of Vicki's antics may serve as either a warning or an inspiration to anyone thinking of keeping a young chimp. It depends upon how much mischief they can tolerate.)

At nine months, Vicki was introduced to an eighteen-month-old boy. In many respects Vicki was more advanced than the boy. Being more agile she had explored her world more thoroughly, had learned to operate various household appliances, tools, and toys, and in general was more experienced than the child. However, she lagged behind in one important respect. The boy could speak a dozen words but Vicki could not use one.

Though Vicki behaved in many ways like a very bright and active human child, her slowness at language was noticeable early in her life. While still lying in her crib she had made sounds that a human baby might, "ooo-ooo-ooo, uh-uh-uh." Unlike a child, she did not enlarge this baby-talk vocabulary as she grew older. Her failure to do so was significant. In a child the babblings and gurglings which are meaningless in themselves serve as a kind of prelanguage training. The infant, as he plays with sound, is actually learning the mechanics of vocalization — how to use breath, tongue, lips, teeth to produce certain kinds of sounds. This practice and experimentation prepares the infant for the next stage in his language development: imitating words he hears, making his first efforts at speech. Vicki, though she was inquisitive and imitative about many other things, showed very little interest in this sound play. In comparison with a child, she was a very silent little creature. Also, though she learned to obey a variety of spoken commands and instructions, she generally showed the same tendency as other apes to be more responsive, more interested in gestures, expressions, and signals than in sound symbols.

This backwardness in making and responding to sounds has been noticed by many others who have observed the apes. The reason for it remains something of a mystery. Just as a chimp's hearing is as keen as a man's, so his vocal apparatus, his mechanical means of producing sound, seems to be about equal to that of humans. In this matter of sound, lack of desire and interest rather than lack of physical ability seems to hold back the ape. Whatever the reason, a young ape does not experiment with sounds as often or as enthusiastically as a child, and this failure plays an important role in later speech development. As time goes on, the ape falls further and further behind the child in his mechanical ability to make different distinct sounds, chiefly, it seems, because of lack of practice.

Not until she was fourteen months old did Vicki learn a

word. It was "mama," the same word that children often learn first, but in Vicki's case the sound did not come easily and naturally from baby-talk gurglings. The Hayeses taught Vicki to say "mama" after hours of instruction. First they repeated the word over and over, but when the little chimp did not imitate the sound as they hoped she would, they held and moved her lips in the proper positions to produce the sound. After she had learned the mechanics of saying "mama" she could and did use her word without help. Later Vicki learned two other words, "cup" and "papa," and she used both with meaning. (When she wanted a drink, she would say "cup.") However, considering the time and effort required to teach Vicki these three words, the prospect of an ape mastering a large sound vocabulary of more complicated words seems very poor.

When she was three years old, the point at which Mrs. Hayes concluded her story of Vicki, the little chimpanzee

Vicki

underwent a thorough testing program. In various problem-solving and general intelligence examinations she seemed to be somewhat more advanced than an average child of the same age. In comparison with other chimpanzees she was understandably more "civilized," quite at home and knowledgeable about many human tools and habits which terrified or puzzled cage-raised chimpanzees. (When she was two years old this cultured little ape slipped away from her guardians and started the motor of the Hayeses' automobile.)

While, with her three words, Vicki was at that time probably the world's most talkative chimpanzee, she was far behind a child of the same age in the matter of language, and this gap was widening at an increasing rate. At three a child's language ability increases dramatically. Then a child begins to learn through language, expressing himself, asking questions, storing up information that he receives when his questions are answered. All of this was beyond Vicki's abilities.

Speech expression is of course only half of communication, the other half being comprehension. At three years Vicki understood many more words than she spoke, responding to fifty or so commands, questions, and announcements. Some of these, as, for example, "get up on the board" (a diaper-changing table) appeared to involve rather complicated language. However, the Hayeses found that often Vicki was responding not to the grammatical content of the sentence but to the tone of voice or a gesture that accompanied it. Vicki was most responsive to short, simple, sharp commands. She became confused if many words were used, confused not only about their meaning but apparently in trying to separate the individual sounds. She showed some, but very little, ability to understand familiar words if they were rearranged in unfamiliar sentences. In short, Vicki understood most words as signals, not as units or symbols of language. If the signals had to do with some actual, immediate situation she responded promptly, but did not show much more talent for understanding abstract expressions than, for example, a dog does. (A dog with a patient master will often understand as many sound signals as Vicki did. Some of these signals, say those used with a hunting or herding dog, involve more complicated instructions than those given to Vicki. However, it should be remembered that dogs, for thousands of years, have been accustomed and selectively bred to respond to commands of men. Given the quick intelligence of the apes, it is likely that if they had lived as close to man for as many years as the dogs, they would surpass dogs in understanding men and making themselves understood.)

Like Vicki, several other apes have been raised in human families and carefully observed. In all cases their language development has been about the same as Vicki's. It is of course always possible that with better teaching methods or a brighter pupil, an ape may one day master a larger vocabulary, both speaking and understanding, than Vicki did. However, presently there is little evidence that any ape can be taught to use language as men do. The apes are intelligent, social creatures. They are among the most able animals when it comes to using the language of reaction, being able to inform others about their feelings toward the real, immediate world with considerable skill and resourcefulness. Occasionally apes have shown some ability to use the kind of abstract symbols which make up our language but in comparison with men their talent in this direction is extremely limited. For example, a chimpanzee can learn as easily as a child to understand the word-signal "open" in connection with some real situation, such as "open the door." However, very rapidly a child, showing both insight and imagination, will come to understand the principle of *open* and the sound "open" will stand as a symbol for this principle. Without much further training or experimentation, a child will apply both the idea and the word "open" not only to one particular door but to all doors, and to windows, boxes, drawers, cans, his mouth as well. Shortly he will be able to make even finer grammatical distinctions, building on the root word "open"; he will begin to comprehend such variations as "opens," "opened," "opening," and "opener." But for the chimpanzee the word "open" will remain a sound signal, associated in his mind with the specific act of opening a door. Only after long and patient training, if ever, will he be able to connect the signal with the general, abstract principle of opening. The language of apes, like that of other animals, consists of a series of disconnected signals. Very seldom are they able to relate one signal to others which modify their meaning, or to create or comprehend sentences and phrases as men do. It has been said that in this matter of communicating through symbolic, reasonable language the apes now stand at the very beginning of a long road down which man has traveled a great distance.

Our talent for our unique language has permitted our race to create what we call culture. Through language, what pleases, pains, profits one man can be made known to many men living in different places, in different ages. The awesome importance of language becomes apparent when we observe the apes who are much like us in many other respects but lack this cultural tool. We have the feeling that we may be watching ourselves as we were before we could use our language, or as we might be if we were stripped of our talent for language.

6
Maybe They Can Talk: Dolphins

Dolphin

WE DON'T have anything in common" is a vague sort of expression often used to explain why a person feels ill at ease with another. This stock phrase frequently camouflages the most brainless sort of snobbery and prejudice (anything strange is dreadful). However, it also expresses an obvious truth. Someone whose experiences, habits, language are similar to our own is easier — at least at first — for us to understand, deal, and communicate with than someone very different from ourselves.

To even a greater degree, this situation influences our feelings about other animals. (The differences between two men, no matter how dissimilar their backgrounds, are really very slight when compared to the difference between any man and a member of any other species.) Generally speaking, we show more sympathy and understanding for the mammals, our closest kin, than we do for the other animals. A mouse, for example, somehow seems more understandable than a brook trout. We see a mouse huddled under a log on a freezing winter's day and we can appreciate the situation of our fellow warm-blooded animal better than we can that of the cold-blooded trout. By the same token we feel that we have more in common with a dog than with a mouse, and for that matter, closer ties with a trout than with an earthworm.

This "like likes like" reaction is understandable, in a sense natural, but it can lead to difficulties. This attitude can stifle our interest, appreciation, and curiosity about other individuals and species whose experiences and style of life are markedly different from our own. Also, creatures who outwardly seem very strange may prove in important "inner" ways to be quite close to us.

The order of Cetacea, which includes whales, dolphins, and porpoises, serves as a good example of how misleading appearance and superficial emotional judgments can be. More than two thousand years ago, Aristotle, the Greek philosopher and naturalist, noted that the Cetacea were not what they seemed to be — fish — but were air-breathing creatures. Today anyone with the slightest interest in natural history knows that the Cetacea are mammals. (The ancestors of the whales left the sea but returned and re-adapted to it rather than remaining on the land like most other mammals.) Nevertheless, the popular feeling persists that regardless of how the whales may be classified scientifically, they are simply a peculiar kind of fish. Furthermore, there has been a tendency, even among land-based naturalists, to assume that since they look like fish and live like fish, the behavior, the "inner life," of the cetaceans is probably as foreign to us as that of the trout.

In the past several decades this view has radically changed. To the astonishment of many, marine biologists have discovered that despite the great differences in appearance and adaptions to their watery environment, the whales seem to be highly intelligent, emotionally sensitive creatures who in some respects (intelligence and their ability to use language, among others) *may* be more like man than even the manlike apes.

Their strange appearance aside, one of the chief reasons that we have been so slow in getting to know the whales and their kin is that they live in an environment in which man is ill at ease, to say the least. Until very recent times our only information about these aquatic mammals came from sailors, whale hunters, and fishermen whose work took them to the edge of haunts of the Cetacea.

Through the centuries mariners have told strange stories about the whales and their very unfishlike behavior. Back on shore, landlubbers, naturalists among them, tended to scoff at these accounts as tall sea tales in a class with whoppers about mermaids and sea monsters. Currently, however, many of the early reports are being re-examined. In light of present knowledge some of them seem to be factual accounts rather than myths.

Several themes, bearing on the question of how and how well cetaceans communicate, thread their way through many of the old tales. There have been persistent accounts of whales displaying what appeared to be highly social as well as intelligent behavior. Whale hunters early noted that these large aquatic mammals roamed the seas in packs or schools, that they hunted co-operatively, driving fish before them as wolves drive deer on land. Whales were also known to band together for their own protection, or to show apparent affection and playfulness toward other members of their group. Whalers, whose usual vantage point for observing the Cetacea was from a harpooner's chair, told of wounding one of these large animals and then being able to kill other members of the school who, rather than fleeing, would return to their dying companion and try to support and assist him in the water.

Another type of story, coming from coastal areas, had to do with those fishlike mammals who apparently wanted to make friends and play with men. In both ancient Greece and Rome there were tales about dolphins, a small member of the Cetacea, coming close to shore, nuzzling and romping with swimmers, occasionally allowing children to ride on their backs. For centuries, "well-informed" men regarded these accounts as sheer fantasy, but in 1955 a dolphin appeared off a New Zealand bathing beach and for two months cavorted, just as supposedly "mythical" Greek and Roman dolphins had. She even allowed children to ride on her back and during her stay became the principal attraction of the resort.

In some respects even more interesting stories are told

Dolphins

about how men and dolphins have apparently co-operated to capture fish. In southern France, in the first century of the Christian era, dolphins were said to have either learned or been trained to assist fishermen who lived near the marshy outlet of a river. As the fishermen set their nets, schools of mullet would seek to escape from the shallow marshy waters. Outside, in the deeper water, the dolphins would wait and, as the fish came out, herd them back toward the men. In return for their help the dolphins would be rewarded with fish, bread, and wine.

A similar story was reported from the Amazon basin. Indians fishing from canoes at night had particular dolphins (fresh-water species) who aided them. The fisherman would call "his" dolphin by giving a whistle or slapping the water with a paddle. The dolphin would appear and chase the fish into the shallow water where the man could spear them. In another story from New Zealand, packs of killer whales, the most feared predators in the sea, would show up off a certain bay every season and drive large humpbacked whales in to the beach where these commercially valuable animals were killed by land-based whale hunters. Again, the killers were rewarded by the men with scraps of food.

The motive behind the dolphins and whales assisting men is not hard to explain. The same sort of relationship exists between certain land mammals. For example, jackals follow lions, gleaning scraps from the big cats' kill. Nevertheless, the co-operation between men and the Cetacea is of great interest. Unlike jackals, who share the lion's range day in and day out, whales and men meet only occasionally and accidentally. That these aquatic mammals should come to understand man's activity indicates a quick intelligence, a learned rather than inherited sort of behavior. Also, with the dolphins it was usually not a matter of lone individuals acting as chance scavengers. Rather, a large school would work together, and in many of the old stories, the school was *summoned* from the deep water when the men were ready to begin their fishing. This suggests that the dolphins had a relatively effective means of communicating between themselves (because they worked together), were responsive to sound signals and quick *to learn* the meaning of new signals. All in all, this relationship between men and dolphins suggests nothing so much as it does that between men and dogs. The playful nature of dolphins and their inclination to hunt in packs make this comparison even stronger. Pondering all these similarities, one scientist suggested that if in the future men should turn more and more to the oceans to supply food for an expanding population, dolphins and other whales may become the shepherds, retrievers, and watchdogs of the sea.

In general the old stories about the cleverness, co-operativeness, and amiability of the whales, particularly the dolphins, are proving, according to the observations of modern naturalists, to be anything but exaggerations. The sociability and intelligence of the dolphin seems to be even greater than was suggested by the so-called myths.

The school is the social unit of the dolphins and appears to be organized somewhat in the fashion of the gorilla tribes described by George Schaller. Dolphin schools, however, may be much larger, sometimes including several hundred individuals. Infant dolphins stay close to their mothers, while adult females and juvenile animals who can care for themselves follow, in a loose sort of way, the lead of an old bull animal. In a practical sense the school enables dolphins together to hunt and defend themselves better than they would be able to do alone. However, there is a great deal of evidence that another reason for the animals traveling and staying together in a unit is companionship, the

Dolphins herding fish

pleasure they take in each other's company. This was the same motive which appeared to influence the gorillas that Schaller observed in the Congo. Dolphins in captivity show unmistakable signs of loneliness, panic, and fear when separated from their companions. Again, as has been observed with chimpanzees, adult dolphins, not necessarily mated animals or parents and offspring, strike up especially strong "friendships" within the school.

The readiness of dolphins to come to the aid of their companions who are in trouble provides another striking example of their sociability. Rescue behavior, though it is attributed to many species of animals in fanciful stories, is actually quite rare. The reaction of most animals when another of their kind meets trouble is to flee. Social fish, birds, even some of the mammals, will often turn cannibal when a member of their group is wounded or injured. Gorillas, chimpanzees, elephants, and, very rarely, dogs have been observed helping their companions in trouble, but this kind of behavior seems most common among two kinds of mammals, men and the Cetacea.

Dolphins must come to the surface of the water to breathe and an injured dolphin who cannot keep afloat will drown just as any land mammal would under water. Therefore the most common first aid given by healthy dolphins to their weakened companions is to get underneath them, push them to the surface, and hold them there so that they can breathe. In the same way, newborn dolphins are often supported at the surface, usually by their mothers but sometimes by other adult animals.

A good if tragic example of this rescue behavior was noted at Marineland of the Pacific, a large marine aquarium in California. A dolphin, Pauline, had been wounded during her capture and was also suffering from shock. She was placed in a tank. Since she was unable to stay on the surface, the first effort of the Marineland attendants was to equip her with a set of "waterwings," two large floats strapped to her body. For three days she lay listlessly in her tank, apparently nearer to death than life. Then a large male dolphin was put in the tank. He immediately showed an interest in Pauline and she responded by making efforts to swim. The waterwings were removed and the male stayed close to Pauline, offering her support as she needed it and, something apparently even more important, sympathy. For two months the animals were inseparable companions. Then, because her wound had not healed properly, Pauline died. The male, obviously missing his companion, circled her body, whistling continuously. He refused to eat and in three days he too died. An autopsy showed that a perforated gastric ulcer was the immediate cause of his death. Though it is perhaps overly sentimental to claim that this male died of grief and loneliness, certainly his refusal to eat after Pauline died aggravated the ulcer.

The "dolphin in distress" behavior gives evidence not only of complex emotions but of intelligence. The act of nudging another animal to the surface shows some ability to react intelligently in an unusual situation, to "diagnose" the condition of the failing animal and recognize the consequences of the situation. The obvious mourning behavior of the Marineland male after Pauline's death is evidence of memory and the ability to deal in some fashion with the abstract idea of loss.

The intelligence of dolphins, their ability to learn, is highly regarded by scientists who have worked closely with these animals, but it is more difficult to test their mentality than that of, say, chimpanzees. Though they breathe air and can be kept out of water for long periods, testing dolphins on land is not much more satisfactory than it would be to require chimpanzees to solve problems in the water. Also, the abilities of dolphins cannot be gauged accurately on the basis of problems designed for creatures like men or apes who are so much different in physique.

However, certain tests that have been devised and many observations made of wild and captive dolphins show real evidence of intelligence. Dolphins learn to push levers for food, to respond to commands and instructions as well as and more quickly than chimpanzees. It has also been demonstrated that they have relatively good memories, and that they learn through imitation and trial and error. Particularly in their play, they show signs of imagination and insight. Dolphins, for example, enjoy playing catch with humans, throwing a ball (knocking it out of the water) to a man and retrieving it when he throws it back. Dolphins have not only been taught this game, but in several instances seem to have "invented" it by themselves, being the one that first throws the ball. This shows some insight into the principle of throwing, as well as some preknowledge of how human beings are likely to behave.

Another curious example of play was observed at Marineland of the Pacific. There captive dolphins were in the habit of playing with formidable moray eels. The dolphins caught the eels, tossed them about, let them go, and recaptured them. Two dolphins, with this sort of game in mind, were trying to pull one of the hiding morays out from under a rock. Unable to get at the eel, one of the dolphins left, killed a scorpion fish (a creature equipped with sharp and poisonous spines) and brought his victim back to the ledge where the moray was hiding. The dolphin, using the dead fish as a prod, probed under the rock until the eel was forced to leave. This action could, of course, have been a lucky, unplanned maneuver on the part of the dolphin, but it also could indicate that dolphins are intelligent enough to invent and use tools.

In trying to gauge the intelligence of the Cetacea, not only the behavior of these animals but the structure of

Blue whale

their brains has been studied. Through surgical examinations it has been learned that the sperm whale has the largest brain of any animal in the world — it weighs more than twenty pounds. The brain of an adult elephant weighs about fifteen pounds and that of a chimpanzee less than a pound. The bottlenosed dolphin (a member of the Cetacea frequently found in marine collections) and man have brains which are approximately the same size — between three and four pounds. The brain is often judged by comparing the weight of the brain to the size and weight of the body whose activities the brain must direct. Measured in this way man is the "brainiest" of animals with the dolphins a close second. In this respect, both surpass the elephants and larger whales.

As yet we simply do not know enough about how and why the miraculously complex brain works to be able, by examination, to determine how intelligent an animal is or what kind of intelligence he has. Therefore the fact that a dolphin's brain is comparable in size and in certain structural features to the human brain does not necessarily mean that dolphin intelligence is similar or equal to that of men.

John Lilly, a physician, biologist, and neurologist, who around 1950 became interested in the Cetacea, their intelligence, behavior, and particularly their language, has examined the brains of many whales and dolphins. He makes the point that with our present knowledge we cannot be certain that creatures with large brains automatically possess great intelligence. However, argues this scientist, we seldom find any biological organ or apparatus which develops without serving some useful function. It is difficult to see why dolphins should have such large brains if they do not use them. If nothing else, the size and structure of the dolphin's brain suggests that these are creatures who deserve considerable further study before any judgment is made on their intellectual capacity.

Being obviously social animals and apparently intelligent ones — perhaps more intelligent than we have previously thought any animal could be — it is natural to assume that the dolphins and other Cetacea have evolved a rather complex system of communication. And it is quite clear that they have. The great question about dolphin communication is similar to the question regarding their intelligence. It is not, Are they intelligent? or, Can they communicate? but, How intelligent are they? and, How well can they communicate?

The method (or at least principal method) by which dolphins communicate is through sounds. The dolphins appear to be among the most vocal of all animals, rivaling in this respect such noisy creatures as birds, bats, and men. The most typical or most noticeable sounds made by dolphins are various whistles. This is the sound they customarily make above the surface of the water and is heard often in aquariums and exhibits when dolphins are directing their vocal efforts toward human observers. Underwater these aquatic mammals can make a great variety of other sounds. Recordings have been made of dolphins' voices and their repertoire includes noises that we might call quacks, squeaks, clicks, creaks, grunts, groans, hisses. The dolphins apparently produce many sounds at extremely high frequencies, beyond the range of the human ear.

Communication aside, there is another important way in which their ability to vocalize and their acute sense of hearing serve the dolphins. Dolphins orientate themselves under water, in a sense "see," by means of sound. As they swim they emit a series of high-pitched sounds which bounce or echo off objects. Hearing these echoes, the dolphins "fix" the position of the object as well as sense its shape and size.

Using this built-in sonar system, captive dolphins have been observed to locate a single BB shot dropped into a large tank of water.

The method by which dolphins apparently communicate, vocalization, is better understood than are the subjects of their communication – what they talk about. Again the problem is the difficulty of observing aquatic creatures in their natural environment. Captive animals produce sounds that express emotions such as pleasure, welcome, playfulness, grief, anger, warning, distress, anxiety. Dolphins in large aquariums seem to respond readily to voice signals of their keepers and in turn produce sound signals for the purpose of attracting attention. This sort of communication is in itself not extraordinary (other mammals perform as well) but it does indicate that dolphins are accustomed to passing along information vocally and receiving it audibly.

Presumably dolphins roaming the seas in large schools have more reason to communicate with each other, more to "say," than do a few animals confined in a small tank. For example, there are the many observations of whales and dolphins hunting in packs, cornering fish in dead-end bays, herding them into shoal waters. These co-operative actions would seem to require considerable communication, certainly as much as displayed by hunting dogs. However, it is impossible to prove how and how much Cetacea in the wild communicate until the actual act of communication – not just actions which seemed based on communication – can be recorded.

Among these stories which seem to provide circumstantial evidence of communication among the Cetacea is one told by whalers.

A fleet of fishing boats working in Antarctic waters was followed by thousands of killer whales. These efficient predators were driving away or killing the fish before the fishermen could take them. Therefore the fleet radioed for assistance, calling in some nearby ships which were equipped with harpoon guns. The first of these ships to arrive on the scene fired one harpoon at the killers. Within a half an hour after this single shot, no killer whales could be found near the harpoon ships any place in the fifty-square-mile fishing area. However, the whales continued to follow the fishing vessels, which were exactly the same design as the hunting boats, except that they lacked the harpoon gun mounted in the bow. This incident strongly suggests intelligent behavior on the part of the killers. After only one experience with the harpoon gun, they realized it was dangerous and learned to recognize the source of danger. Secondly, it seems that the killers who first encountered the harpoon ships communicated with other members of the pack, passing along enough information for their companions to be able to identify the harpoon-carrying ships.

Interesting as such stories are, their true significance cannot be judged until equipment is devised which will enable marine biologists to make the kind of detailed, long-term observations of whales in their natural environment that George Schaller made of gorillas. While a dictionary of whale or dolphin is still to be compiled, most scientists who are familiar with these animals assume that in time we will be able to assign definite meanings to a number of sounds which these aquatic mammals produce. The real mystery now seems to be what kind, rather than how much, language these animals have. Is the language of the Cetacea (and particularly the dolphins) simply a good example of the language of reaction that is used by other mammals — a series of disconnected signs and signals, which are produced and understood in response to immediate, real situations? Or is it possible that these animals might use language somewhat after the fashion of men, communicating by means of symbols which they learn and which they modify so as to convey and comprehend abstract information?

These questions have especially interested John Lilly, whose studies of the brains of whales and dolphins have led him to consider the ability (or lack of it) of these animals to communicate in a reasonable, intelligent manner. In 1961 Lilly published a book, *Man and Dolphin,* in which he described his reasons for investigating the higher language abilities of dolphins. Since then, John Lilly has had the reputation of being the "dolphin man," a sort of mad scientist who claims he can talk to whales. Many of the humorous and critical comments on the work of this scientist seem to have been made by those who have not studied or understood Lilly's reports on his work.

Neither in his book nor in scientific articles has Lilly claimed that he has talked or ever will talk with dolphins. What he has suggested is that since we have yet not proved dolphins *cannot* use language as men do and since there are indications that they are very intelligent, vocal animals, the whole question deserves serious study and thought.

Though John Lilly finds the size of the dolphin's brain impressive, he does not claim that this alone guarantees that these animals can reason and communicate as men do. However, he does believe that a brain which weighs less than two and a half pounds (that of a chimpanzee, for example) is probably too small to permit its owner to use the language of reason (or intellectual communication, according to Lilly's definitions). He argues that on this basis, if we are to find animals other than man who can communicate intelligently, we will find them among either the elephants or members of the whale family.

Several other factors influenced Lilly in selecting the dolphins for his studies in animal communication. The evidence offered by examination of their brains is reinforced by the somewhat scanty observations of their behavior. They do seem to act with remarkable intelligence. Their large brains do not appear to have evolved simply for decoration or to amuse scientists. Also, since they can produce a wide range of sounds and appear to respond well to vocal signals, they at least have the mechanical ability to deal with a vocal language as we humans do.

One of the great differences between our language (that of reason or intellect) and that of other animals is that we *learn* to use most of the symbols of our language. Other animals seem to *inherit* the ability to make and comprehend the signs of their languages. Thus normal puppies, even if raised alone, will make and respond to many of the same signs that are used by dogs who have grown up in the company of others of their kind. However, a child isolated from conventional language (a deaf-mute, for example) will either not use language or will develop a private sort of language incomprehensible to others. Also, to use dogs again as an example, though the signs of dog language vary somewhat depending upon environment, they are, in general, universal. The language that a child learns depends, of course, completely upon what he is taught. A Chinese child will learn an entirely different set of language symbols from those learned by a child born and raised in the United States.

In light of this difference, John Lilly reasons that *if* an animal does or can use the language of reason then the young must learn it from adults, as a child does, not inherit the language, as a puppy does. Furthermore, if a dolphin can learn his own language (presumably made up of a variety of sound symbols) then he should be able to learn other vocal languages – English, for example. Since dolphins and men are different in so many ways, the teaching process would certainly not be as easy or natural as an English-speaking child being taught to speak Chinese, but the principle would be the same.

Working on these assumptions, John Lilly reasoned that if he could teach a dolphin to use and comprehend a human language, this would serve as proof that these animals communicated among themselves using a learned language and that their intellectual capacity was somewhat similar to that of man, more similar than that displayed by any other animals.

The same sort of proof could be claimed if a dolphin were able to teach dolphin language to a scientist such as John Lilly. However, the question of motive aside, a man would make a very poor underwater student. Dolphins are more adaptable, being able to hear and vocalize in the air better than men are able to do in the water.

Around 1955 John Lilly started the work which still occupies him, trying either to establish vocal, reasonable communication with dolphins or to prove such communication impossible. (In every pioneering study, negative as well as positive results are important. If Lilly eventually

Dolphins

shows that reasonable communication with dolphins is impossible, this will answer the question of their ability as certainly as if he had proved such communication is possible. However, it is much easier to show that a thing is possible than it is to demonstrate that something is absolutely impossible. Therefore positive findings are the objective of most scientific experiments, while negative results serve as a useful by-product.)

Among other devices Lilly used in his aquatic laboratory was an arrangement of air and underwater microphones attached to amplifiers and recording devices. One of the purposes of this intercom system was to familiarize dolphins with the sound patterns of human voices, not only with words, commands, and instructions spoken directly to the animals but with general conversation between members of the research staff. Also this system permitted the staff to eavesdrop on whatever vocalizations the dolphins made under water. By studying recordings of these sounds it was found that the dolphins seemed to be making efforts to imitate human voices. The longer a dolphin was exposed to human conversation (particularly if he were isolated from other dolphins) the more frequently he would be heard to make "humanoid" sounds, sounds unlike those of dolphinese. Human laughter, for example, attracted the dolphins' attention and they frequently seemed to be mimicking it.

On one occasion, while a male dolphin was "listening in," John Lilly was dictating technical data into a recorder. The abbreviation "T R R" was used frequently during this dictation. Later, in studying tapes from the underwater microphone, the dolphin was heard to quack, quite clearly, "T R R." Under similar circumstances this same animal repeated the words "three hundred and twenty."

One curious (or as John Lilly writes, mysterious) example of dolphin mimicry was recorded in 1960. Two dolphins,

Baby and Lizzie, who had been companions in a tank, were separated because Lizzie was in poor health. Lilly, anxious about the ailing animal, had stayed late near their pens. Someone called loudly to him that he would miss dinner, that "It's six o'clock."

"The tape recorded this on the air channel," writes Lilly in *Man and Dolphin*. "In a few seconds on the underwater channel, Lizzie, near the hydrophone, put-putted, Baby answered with a short fast series of whistles, and Lizzie very loudly came out with a humanoid sentence, the meaning of which (if any) has puzzled several of us since. It may have been a poor copy of 'It's six o'clock.' But I was caught first by another meaning. It sounded to me like 'This is a trick' with a peculiar hissing accent. Other people have since heard the tape and came to the same conclusion."

A less mysterious but perhaps more significant report on the dolphin's ability to mimic the human voice was made by John Lilly in 1965. Two dolphins participated in a series of tests. First they were trained (by being rewarded when they were successful) to imitate a short burst of human sound, not words, but nonsense syllables. Then a list of 198 of these syllables was prepared. In various sequences and series the syllables were recited to the dolphins. Their replies were recorded. Over a period of several months it was found that in 92 per cent of the tests the dolphins' replies came within one syllable of equaling the number of sound bursts they had heard. In 71 per cent of the tests the dolphins repeated exactly the same number of syllables they had heard. The quality of the sounds produced by the dolphins was analyzed by human listeners and by audiometric devices. It was clear that the dolphins were not replying in sound bursts of pure dolphinese but were modifying their voices to imitate humans. The length of the sound bursts also corresponded to the length of the individual sounds that the human speaker had produced.

These tests demonstrated that dolphins are among the great vocal mimics of the animal world. ". . . even parrots and mynah birds," wrote Lilly of these tests, "apparently do not give such large numbers of replies and such sustained accurate performance. To date only dolphins and humans share this ability."

On the basis of these and other observations it seems probable that in time men will be able to teach dolphins to mimic more complex human sounds, to speak more clearly than they have been heard to before. However, even if this is accomplished and dolphins learn to speak in human phrases and sentences, there is still the question of what kind of speech the animals are using. Are they merely imitating meaningless (to them) sounds, performing as immensely talented parrots, or can they be associating abstract meaning with the vocal symbols — communicating intelligently, using the language of reason?

As yet these questions simply cannot be answered. We do not know enough about dolphins and other members of the Cetacea. Still, the fact that there is not a clear answer to this problem is in itself important. With all other animals whose communicative ability has been carefully observed, the conclusion has been reached that they cannot use the language of reason, that they lack the intellectual ability to do so — they are largely restricted to communication through the language of reaction. With dolphins the issue is in doubt. Because of what we have learned of their behavior and intelligence, because of work done by John Lilly and others in regard to their ability to vocalize, the possibility remains that these animals can use language as we do. At the moment, investigating this possibility is perhaps the most exciting and important study in the field of animal communication.

7
Learning the Language of Animals

Blue whale

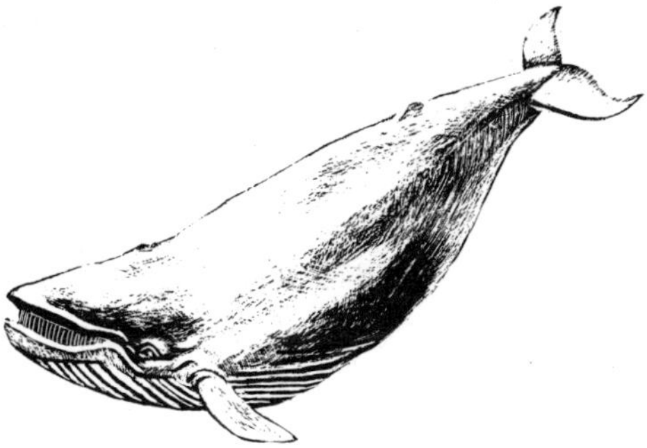

Who can communicate with animals?

Anyone who has opened the door in response to a cat's mewing cry to be let in, or had a dog come in answer to a whistle, has communicated with animals. Anyone who has heard two quail alternating "Bob-Bob-Whites" from opposite ends of a field has heard animals communicating with each other.

All animals have some sort of language by which they pass information between each other. Men have learned a little of the vocabulary of many of these languages just as some animals have learned to understand signals which men make. Nevertheless, it is safe to say that we do not understand or even recognize all the communicative signs that any animal, even the most familiar, uses. Because com-

Quail

munication is a kind of behavior which can be observed in almost any place where there are animals and because there is much still to be learned, the study of animal languages fascinates professional scientists, students, part-time and amateur naturalists.

Most of the examples of animal communication referred to in this book have been first observed and analyzed by professionals who have the time, equipment, and training to do so. An amateur would seldom have the opportunity or necessary background to make the observations of gorilla language that George Schaller did in the Congo or to perform the kind of experiments with dolphins that John Lilly has in his marine laboratories.

Often, however, a beginning or amateur naturalist can repeat communication observations made by professionals, and in doing so can increase both his understanding and appreciation of animal languages. Anyone with access to a beehive and sufficient patience can make many of the experiments that led Karl von Frisch to the discovery of the marvelous dancing language of the bees. Opportunities to camp next to a den of arctic wolves, as Farley Mowat did, are rare. However, many of the signs and signals he observed being made by these wild members of the canine family are also made, in modified form, by domestic dogs.

If he is sufficiently patient, observing, and informed, it is quite possible for the nonprofessional to make original observations and contribute new understanding of animal communication. Exotic creatures, gorillas, whales, wolves, catch our imagination, but there is often as much to be learned from the more familiar ones. Animal communication can be studied in an aquarium, a pigeon loft, an anthill, or a stone wall where chipmunks play. In North America, perhaps the most common mammals, and among the most interesting, are the tiny shrews. Yet as far as behavior goes they are among the least known.

There is a great opportunity and need for more observations of the behavior, communicative and otherwise, of wild, free-living animals. Many of our theories of animal communication are based on observations of captive specimens, simply because it is often so hard to keep free creatures under scrutiny. Yet many scientists admit that this is an unsatisfactory arrangement. For example, much has been written about social rank among animals (pecking orders, for example) and the language by which status is expressed. However, it has been suggested that perhaps the importance and frequency of this kind of behavior has been exaggerated because so many of the records involve captive animals. Perhaps status behavior is more important to animals confined in restricted territories than it is to their free-living relatives.

Making observations of true wild life requires great patience and persistence. These qualities amateur naturalists can supply, even though they may lack complicated equipment and the time for wilderness expeditions. One of the reasons that we know so much about bird language, in comparison with that of other animals, is because there are so many amateur ornithologists who have contributed much valuable information. Dictionaries of the visual and vocal signs of many common animals are still to be compiled. The need is for sufficient man hours of field observation.

The mark of a serious field naturalist, professional or amateur, is a set of good notes. Casual observations, based on memory, unrelated to time, place, and circumstances, may make interesting conversation but they are otherwise of little value. Notes not only preserve a naturalist's own observations, but aid others who may have observed or may want to observe the same phenomena. If one observes a happening which strikes him as unusual or significant and makes accurate notes, then others, using the notes as a guide, can perhaps repeat the observation and verify its importance.

Common though it is, animal communication is difficult to observe and record accurately. Any two people who can use a rule and scale will make almost identical observations on the size and weight of an animal. However, when it comes to recognizing language signs and particularly assigning meanings to them, observations will vary because they are subjective. Making notes on animal language involves a constant struggle with our own language, trying to describe the meaning of what one has seen or heard with the greatest possible objectivity. Modern techniques of photography and sound recording have greatly aided in the study of animal communication, but the value of these mechanical notes still depends largely on the judgment of the observer. Also, even a photo or a record alone does not constitute a meaningful note. The recording of a bird song

Shrew and dragonfly

must be accompanied by information about the sex, age, status, and territory of the singer, the time of the year, time of day, and other background circumstances.

A great deal of very bad information about animal communication has been reported in so-called "nature stories." One lingering look from a dog will be said to express a complicated, sentimental mood. A bird song will be translated into a stanza of poetry. Such observations tell us little about the state of the inner animal, though somewhat more about the man who made the observations. To learn any simple sign of an animal's vocabulary, one must first observe the identical sign repeatedly, note the circumstances that apparently stimulate the animal, and the reaction of the animal (or that of others). Self-discipline and again patience are as necessary for learning crow as they are for Chinese.

For a beginner, one of the best ways to learn something about animal communication in general is to concentrate on learning the language of one particular species. In selecting an animal language for close study, there are several practical matters that should be considered. First, the animal should be available. If one wants to learn something of bird language in my area of southern Pennsylvania, the crow or quail, both of which are common, are better species than the pileated woodpecker, which is scarce. As a rule, beginners should avoid trying to specialize in rare and secretive creatures. Too much time and energy must be spent just in finding the animal and getting into a position from where he can be observed.

The first animals selected should be better than average communicators. Ducks are better equipped, for example, to tutor a student in bird language than are solitary hawks, whom one may watch for hours without seeing any sign of communication. If animals are to be caged then their cageability is a factor. The mountain on which I live supports at least two bobcat families, young of which could probably be secured. However, I do not have the inclination or equipment for penning up a bobcat. Even if I were able to, a bobcat would make an extremely poor observation animal. Caged, these cats seem to suffer from perpetual shock. In confinement their behavior is abnormal, to say the least.

Everything else being equal, one should select an animal toward whom one feels the greatest sympathy and emotional attachment. In my area, for example, there are many sorts of available, social, communicative insects, amphibians, songbirds, and rodents. Yet I have ignored these interesting animals in order to learn a little of fox, crow, shrew, owl, and hawk language. It is a personal matter. It takes a long time to learn a few words of animal language. It is a good idea to start learning from an animal whom you feel you would like to have as a friend.

• • • •

Why communicate with animals?

Perhaps the truest explanation (if not reason) for our persistent interest in animal communication is that it arises from curiosity. Our curiosity began long before there was any science or even any name for such things as animal behavior and animal psychology. Simply in watching and listening to animals the idea grew that these creatures must be saying something to each other and comprehending what others were saying. Men became obsessed with finding out what the animals were talking about for no better (or worse) reason than that they wanted to know. The same curiosity is still with us. If anything, we are more interested now than ever before in eavesdropping on the conversations of animals.

Several centuries ago man's insatiable curiosity was formalized, dignified, and titled – given the name "research" or "pure science." The motives, if not the methods, of the research scientists are different from those of applied scientists. The latter are concerned with adapting what is known, principles and phenomena, to serve what we regard as useful, practical ends. The research scientist seeks simply to know what is not known. For example, Niko Tinbergen, whose work with herring gulls is mentioned in Chapter Three, is one of the greatest research scientists of our time. Yet Tinbergen's work does not have much "practical" value, nor does he claim that it has. This Dutch scientist spent hundreds of wet, cold hours watching gulls because he wanted to know more about them than he did (or anyone else did). He is a curious man.

The principal reason that men are trying to find out how bees, birds, apes, whales, and many other animals use language is that they suspect that much that can be known is unknown. This is the challenge and motive. This is curiosity.

The research scientists and others driven by the need to

know are sometimes ridiculed because they are "impractical." However, this kind of criticism is heard less frequently now than it once was. We have found, through very practical experience, that even the queerest, most unpromising sorts of knowledge have a way of proving unexpectedly useful. For example, many of the intensely practical techniques of modern agriculture are based on the discoveries of an Austrian monk, Gregor Mendel, who was simply curious about the principles of heredity. So it is with many of the studies of animal communication. They are not undertaken for "practical" reasons but simply to expand knowledge. However, it would be very risky to prophesy that none of the discoveries growing out of this research will be useful.

To date, perhaps the most practical application of our knowledge of animal languages has been to increase the ease and efficiency with which we deal with domestic animals. The working partnership between men, dogs, horses, elephants, hawks, and many other animals would have been impossible without the development of a language that both parties could understand. It can be assumed that as we learn more about the language of these and other old animal companions, the companionship will become closer and the partnership more useful.

There is also reason to believe that better communication with animals will enable us to form practical associations with animals heretofore regarded as "wild." It has been suggested (and some experiments have been conducted along these lines) that apes, baboons, and monkeys could perform certain simple, repetitive tasks more efficiently than men and suffer less from boredom. Accomplishing this would depend largely on our ability to give instructions, to communicate with the animal employees. As mentioned in the last chapter, some believe that dolphins, if we can solve our language problems, may one day serve men in the water as dogs do on land, as hunters, herders, and companions. Also, it is not inconceivable that dolphins might be enlisted in the military service. It is perhaps too much to expect these aquatic mammals to disarm a submarine as a dog will a burglar, but even if their intelligence and communicative ability is no greater than that of dogs, they might be instructed to detect and report unusual objects.

All of this — baboons harvesting fruit, dolphins serving in the navy — may seem somewhat fantastic. However, the chances are that the men who first suggested that dogs might be commanded to retrieve game, elephants ordered to stack logs, or horses given directions, were probably told to forget their fantastic notions and devote themselves to practical matters.

There is still another way in which the study of animal communication may prove useful to men. Language, for men as well as animals, is an outward indication of inner mood, motives, mental processes, and emotions. Using language as a key, we are interested in entering into this inner

Gulls

life of animals; first, for the same reason we are interested in the language itself, because of curiosity. Secondly, there is reason to believe that the better we understand the behavior of the other animals, the better we may be able to understand our own behavior, and perhaps improve upon it. Robert Yerkes's comment that men might well profit if they could learn the secret of the chimpanzees' apparent emotional stability and social poise is a case in point. Animal caste and rank, friendships, fears, are other phenomena which might well be compared with seemingly corresponding behavior in men.

The way language is used is one of the prime indicators of the quality of the inner life of an animal. Thus, there is no test by which we can definitely prove that a chimpanzee does not deal with abstract symbols in an imaginative way (or deals with them only feebly). However, the failure of these apes to use and respond to an intellectual language provides strong circumstantial evidence that they do not have these abilities. If John Lilly were to show that dolphins communicate by means of an intellectual language, the conclusion would follow that, like men, the dolphins are reasonable, intelligent creatures. The significance of such a discovery would be immense.

Throughout history, man's relationship with other animals has been based on the premise that we and we alone are intelligent. The classical definition of man is that he is a (and *the*) rational animal. Because of this supposed special status, we have given to ourselves many special rights, decreeing that there are two entirely different ethical systems governing relationships between living things — one operating between man and man, another between men and animals. A man who steals a rational animal from his parents is called a kidnapper, but a man who captures a young irrational animal is a zoological collector. A man who owns a rational animal is despised as a slave master, but the keeper of an irrational animal is a pet lover, herdsman, or zoo director. Irrational animals are killed in the name of sport, research, agriculture, pest control, but when man kills man it is murder.

So much depends upon the assumption of man's being the only rational animal, capable of intelligent behavior, that if the definition were proved false the consequences would radically affect our entire view of the world. If, for example, a scientist one day carries on an intelligent conversation with a dolphin, thus proving that dolphins too are rational animals, we will be immediately faced with the question of what are the religious, political, and economic rights and responsibilities of these animals. We would have to re-examine our entire moral position not only in respect to dolphins, but in regard to the entire living, nonhuman world. To say the least, many long-standing philosophical beliefs and ethical principles would have to be altered or abandoned.

John Lilly, who has thought deeply about the significance of his experiments with dolphins, suggests still another reason for attempting to communicate with these and other animals. It is not inconceivable, speculates this scientist, that sometime in the future we may encounter intelligent creatures totally alien to this planet. These creatures may be far stranger in appearance and behavior than the dolphins, far more intelligent, and perhaps less amiable. If such an encounter should occur, men might find it very much to their advantage to have had some previous practice in establishing language contact with alien intelligences. The methodology of learning dolphinese (if there is such a language), not what men and dolphins had said to each other, would in such a hypothetical situation be the important thing.

Crow

Curiosity, economics, and space travel aside, there remains, at least for me, one final answer to the question, Why communicate with animals? The better we understand an animal and make ourselves understood to him, the more likely we are to treat him with toleration, dignity, and affection. To me this is important. Whatever our rights and status in regard to other animals, we humans are clearly the dominant species on the planet. With our power, it seems to me there *should* go responsibility — the responsibility to respect and protect life in all its various forms.

I have spent some time, for example, listening to and watching the language of crows. Occasionally I have been able to express myself to them. This has given me considerable pleasure, in some ways not unlike the pleasure to be had in commonplace conversation with a human friend. The experience has also made me think of and feel what I consider to be my responsibility toward the animal world. I believe most people who take the time to learn a little of any of the animal languages will be affected in much the same way.

Reading About Animal Communication

Communication is a specialized form of behavior. Animal languages therefore can only be understood and appreciated in terms of animal behavior. There are many books and articles on the behavior of various animals. Two good reference books on general behavior are: *Animals as Social Beings*, by Adolf Portmann; and *Animal Behavior*, by John Paul Scott. Both books include extensive bibliographies for the reader who is interested in more specialized and technical reports.

In *King Solomon's Ring*, by Konrad Lorenz, animal behavior, particularly communication, is described in a series of character studies of animals whom the author has known intimately. Konrad Lorenz has been one of the most influential scientists in the study of animal behavior. In his delightful writings about animals he can adopt a casual, familiar style because his knowledge of them is so vast.

Karl von Frisch was the first to learn the language of the bees and his book *The Dancing Bees* not only describes communication among these insects, but the way in which his discoveries were made. *Communication among Social Bees* was written by Martin Lindauer, a student of Von Frisch's. This book reports on some of the observations of bee language made since the publication of *The Dancing Bees*.

Perhaps more has been written about the behavior and communication of birds than any other class of animals. *A Study of Bird Song*, by Edward A. Armstrong, is an encyclopedic book on the vocal behavior and language of birds. There are many other books which deal with single species of birds. In this category, *The Herring Gull's World*, by Niko Tinbergen, is regarded as a classic. It not only describes in detail the behavior and language of the gull, but gives some idea of the patience and ingenuity required to make such a thorough study of any species of animal.

Konrad Lorenz's *Man Meets Dog* is an entertaining but extraordinarily informative book on the development, behavior, and language of domestic dogs. Farley Mowat, like Lorenz, is a naturalist with a sense of humor; *Never Cry Wolf* describes his experiences and observations while spending a season with arctic wolves. *Dog Obedience Training*, by Milo Pearsall and Charles G. Leedham, is one of many good books on dog training. These emphasize how the partnership between men and dogs is based on the ability to communicate.

Despite our long interest in the apes, information on these animals is scarce in comparison to that available on other species. *The Great Apes* by Robert M. Yerkes, published in 1929, remains one of the best general books on these animals. *Chimpanzees,* by the same author, is an account of experimental work with these apes conducted in laboratories. *The Ape in Our House,* by Cathy Hayes, is a good account of the failures, frustrations, and limited successes involved in trying to teach a young chimpanzee to use and respond to human language. Our understanding of the apes has suffered from the lack of good observation of these animals in the wild. Two books by George Schaller, *The Year of the Gorilla* and *The Mountain Gorilla,* both written following his field experiences in Africa, are among the very best.

John Lilly has been a pioneer in the study of dolphin intelligence and communication, actual and potential. His book, *Man and Dolphin,* describes his own work and also contains a good reference list of books and scientific articles on the subject. In *Dolphins: The Myth and the Mammal,* Antony Alpers has collected many of the old and new stories having to do with the behavior of the Cetacea.

About the Author

Bil Gilbert, a member of the American Society of Mammalogists, studied zoology at George Washington University. He co-operates with the U.S. Fish and Wildlife Service in their program for banding and recording data on the birds of prey, has collected small mammals along the Mexican-Guatemalan border for deposit in the Smithsonian Institution, has organized and promoted various conservation efforts, and has acted as a Peace Corps consultant in survival and outdoor training.

Mr. Gilbert contributes numerous articles to such magazines as *Sports Illustrated, Boys' Life, Esquire, The New York Times Magazine*, and *Saturday Evening Post*. His principal avocational interests are white-water canoeing, falconry, and speleology.

He lives in Iron Springs, Pennsylvania, with his wife, Ann, and their four children, as well as raccoons, dogs, hawks, and other creatures.